The tunes are written in the children's best chest-register (the D – B hexachord  pitch is absolutely fixed. In fact it is advisable to try the same tune in another dictation of *sol-fa* letters or from hand-signs – but of course only if this is possible from staff notation one must stick to the correct pitch – especially if the pupils read otherwise his internal hearing will become confused.

It is not advisable to start in C major as many children find the treble C a st...

The printed copy does not indicate the elements of the melodic structure. This sets a minor problem... ... be identified. On the other hand three-bar phrases are marked. In some places repeats are given in full so that the eye becomes accustomed to recognising identical musical phrases quickly. We depend on the fascinating effect of small differences – "Similar but not the same": the child's attention should be captured by either a formula in the tune which is repeated with a slight difference, or by a reference to a well-known tune.

To begin with there are no key signatures as, in any case, the *do* is given. A tune consisting of merely two notes can bear different tonal interpretations. We have chosen the easiest; the nearest to pentatonic completeness. Later on key signatures are introduced which have no effect on the tune but assist in the identification of the *do*. To identify the *do* within the five-note system (pentatone), anyone not familiar with key signatures should look out for the three adjacent notes or tritone. Again, there are no *tempo* indications. Generally a quarter note (crotchet) should equal a normal walking step. At first reading this could be slower, but always in rhythm! Most of the tunes are not tied to one tempo, so later on they can be taken at a faster pace.

Four-fifths of the tunes do not go outside the six-note compass. Pentatonic tunes usually cover a wider compass – there are some of two octaves. Ours (the Hungarian) vary between a nine and twelve note compass and are therefore not suitable for children. In many cases the rhythm is also very difficult. In flourishing pentatonic systems one finds many tunes of limited compass and simple rhythm. In our country this type of tune has almost disappeared. It was driven out by the appearance of Indo-Germanic children's songs and by "artificial" children's songs of foreign inspiration, either homemade or imported via the schools.

If we want our heritage of folksong to regain its old attraction, shining out over the whole nation, we have to prepare our children for it with tunes of limited compass and easy rhythm, but ones with the spirit and structure of the old folksongs. The alternative is that, having studied the fashionable music text books, they will find the nation's oldest music unfamiliar – as many of them do now.

The reason is that it is a wrong method to start from the diatonic system and then return to the pentatonic one as though it were an exceptional oddity, not to mention the fact that there are still school music books that pay no attention to the pentatonic system, though this alone could be our natural foundation-stone. It is one of the axioms of sound education to move from the simple towards the complex. It may be difficult for slaves to a foreign and out-of-date seventy year-old system to get accustomed to it, but we hope that every conscientious teacher will do his utmost to make the chaotic transition period as brief as possible.

Those who have already started with the C major method will find a bridge toward the pentatonic system at around exercise **215**. The proper thing to do is then to look out for the diatonic system from there onwards.

We still have a long way to go from our small tunes to the *"Solfège de concours"* of the Paris Conservatoire. Only an expert can do it. But both expert and music lover start equal if they start well. Up to now I have wanted to help the youngest. But adults can also be pupils as "there is no royal road to learning".

Zoltán Kodály. September 1943

1943 – it was not the proper time for basic reforms. Following all the world-shaking events there was still a great deal happening that hampered development.

But finally the seeds were sprouting. The "singing schools" came into existence, with singing lessons every day, yielding excellent results not only in singing but in all subjects. When all the schools become "singing" ones we shall have real education for everyone. At present there are a hundred of them working under the auspices of the (Hungarian) Ministry of Education.

The "333" became the modest beginning of a respectable literature. Many people used it to learn to read music. Many more could have done so had more professors realised the advantages of the *sol-fa* edition and used both in parallel. I do not know of a better exercise than the transposition of notes into letters and vice-versa, both in writing and orally. The present edition aims to facilitate this. The children should sing the music in staff notation to *sol-fa*, and the music in *sol-fa* to the fixed pitch letter-names (A-B-C) always in different but predetermined keys and invariably at the actual pitch level; if we say C it should really be C.

This is the way towards acquiring the sense of absolute pitch. Only lively musical activity can produce a musical expert. Listening to music is by itself insufficient.

I hope that in its new form this book of exercises will contribute to our aim of making music available to everybody.

Zoltán Kodály. March 1961

N.B. There are minor differences in this edition in **193, 195, 196, 198** and **199**.

333 READING EXERCISES

Revised English Edition
taken from 1966 Hungarian Edition

ZOLTÁN KODÁLY

(1882 - 1967)

*This sign indicates a three-bar phrase

B. & H. 19977

2

4

B. & H. 19977

38 rd l,
2/4
d d d d r d l, d d d d r l, r r r r d r d l, l, r r d d
39
2/4
d r l, d d d r l, d d d r d l, l, d r r d r l,
40 3
2/4
r l, r d r d l, 3 d l, d r d l, d 3 d d d d r r l, r
41
2/4
r d r l, r d l, d l, l, l, l, d d r d r l,
42
2/4
l, l, d l, r r r r l, l, d l, r r d d d d r l, l, r r d r l, l,
43
2/4
d l, r l, d d l, r l, d d d d d r r r d d r d l,

mrd
50
m r m r d m r r r m m r m r d r m d r m m r m r d r d d
51
m r m m r m m r d r m d r d r m d
52
m r d r m m r d r m r r r r m d r r r r d
53
d r m r d r d r m r d r m d r d r m m d r d r d
54
r m m r m m r m m r m m m r d r m r d r d r r m m d d
55
r r r r d d r r r r d d m r d r m r d r m d m m r r

9

B. & H. 19977

r d l, s,
62
3
s, r | d r | l, l, l, :|| s, s, s, s, | d d | r l, | s, s, s, s, | d l, | s, s, ||
63
s, s, | r r | d r d l, | s, :|| l, l, l, l, | d l, | r r d r | l, | s, s, | r r | d r d l, | s, ||
64
s, s, d | r r | d d l, | s, s, :|| l, l, | l, l, | l, r | l, | s, s, d | r r | d d l, | s, ||
65
d s, d | r d | s, :|| l, l, l, l, | l, d s, | l, s, l, | d r | d ||
66
r r l, | r r d | ||: r l, s, | d d d :|| r d s, | l, l, l, ||
67
s, s, s, | d d d | r r d | l, l, l, | r r d | l, l, d | r d l, | s, s, s, ||
68
s, d | r r | d r d | s, | s, l, | d d | r d s, | l, ||

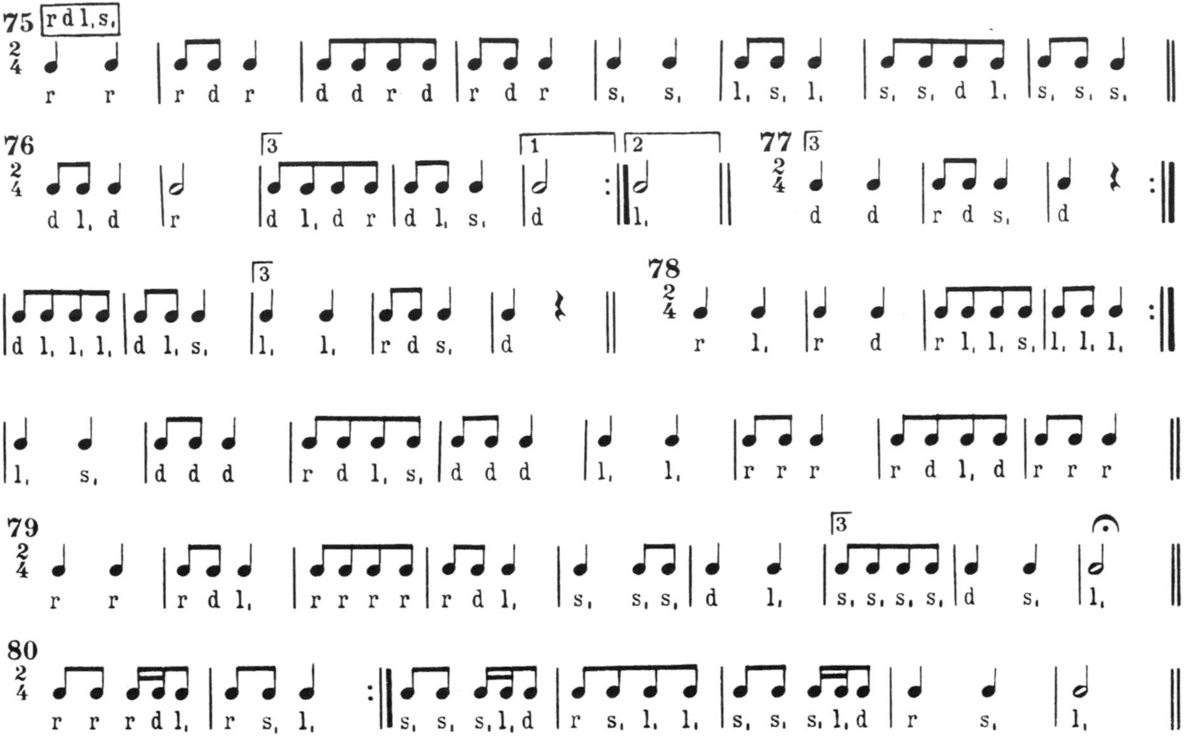
75
r d l, s,
76
77
78
79
80

87
r d l, s,
2/4
s, l, d s, l, d r r r r d l, r d l, s, s, d r d l, r d l, s, s, s,
88
3
2/4
d r d l, d s, l, s, l, l, d l, s, r r d d r d l, d s, d
89
2/4
s, s, l, l, s, l, s, d d s, d d r d l, s, s, d d d
90
2/4
s, l, l, l, l, s, s, d r r r r d d l, l, d r r l, l, s, s, l, s, d d d
91
2/4
r r r r d l, r s, s, s, s, d l, s, l, l, d l, s, s, l, l, r r d l, s,
92
2/4
r d r l, r d r l, d d l, s, d l, s, l, l, r

16

B. & H. 19977

18

B. & H. 19977

122 | r d l, s,

r d l, r d l, | s, s, s, : s, l, l, l, | r l, d | r d l, s, l, | s, s, s,

123

s, l, d r d l, | s, s, d : r r d d | r r s, | d l, r d l, | s, s, s,

124

s, s, l, s, | s, d r | r d l, s, | l, l, s, : r r | d l, d | d d r d | s, s, s, :

125

s, l, d l, | s, s, s, | s, l, d l, | s, s, s, | d d d d | r r l, | s, l, d l, | s, s, s,

126

l, s, l, r | d l, s, | l, s, l, r | d d | d d r d | l, s, d | r r d r | l, l,

127

s, s, r d l, | s, : r r r r | d r d | s, s, d d | r r l, | s, s, r | d l, | s,

22

24

26

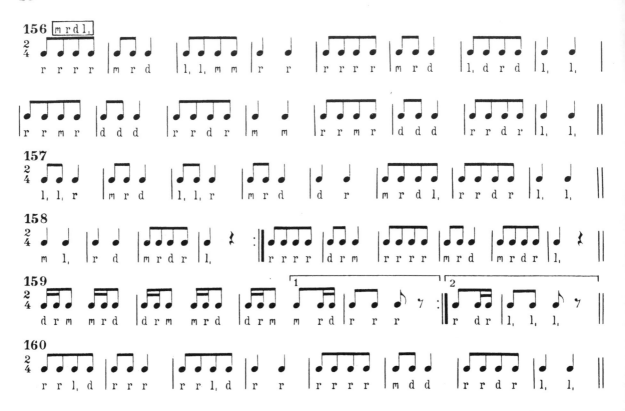

30

189 m r d l, s,
s, l, | d l, s, | l, | d r | m r d | r | d r | m r r l, | s, d | r l, s, | l,
190
s, l, s, | s, l, s, | d d r r | m r d | d r m | r d l, | d d r r | d l, s,
191
d r m | m r d | r s, | d d d d | r d l, | s, | s, d r r | r m r | d
192
l, l, l, l, | m m | r m | m r d r | d s, | l, l, | m r d r | d l, | s, d | m r d r | d s, | l, l,
193
s, m | r d l, | s, | r r r r | m d | d d d d | r l, | s, m | r d l, | s,
194
d l, | s, m r | d | s, s, s, s, | l, m | m m m m | s, r | d l, | s, m r | d

34

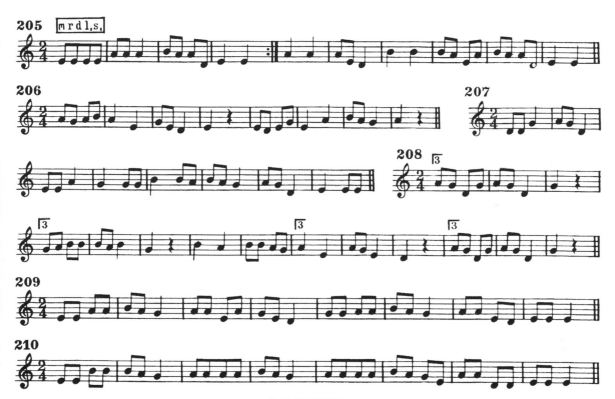

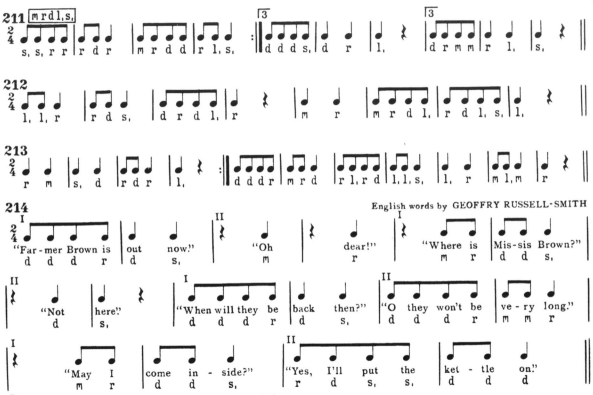

English words by GEOFFRY RUSSELL-SMITH

B. & H. 19977

38

40

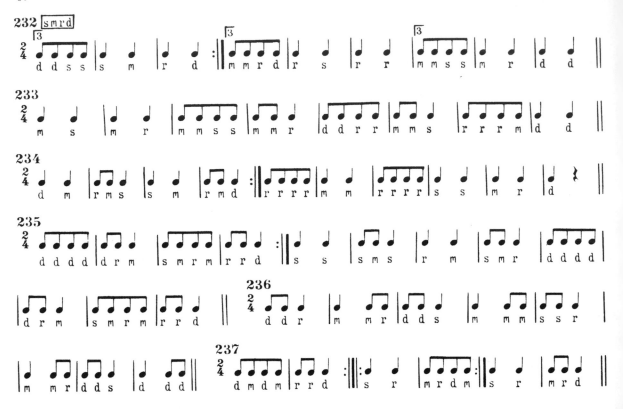

42

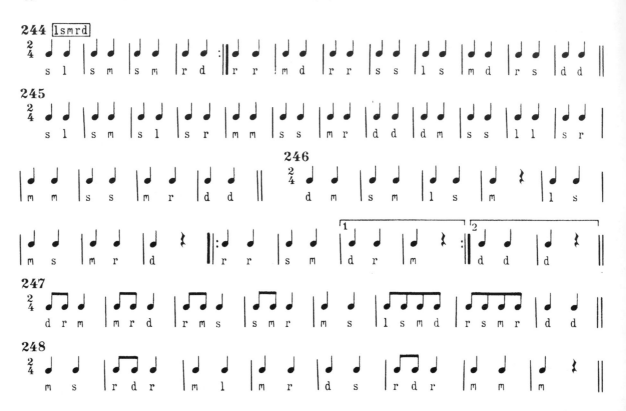

244 `lsmrd`

44

255 <u>lsmrd</u>

256

257

258

259

260

B. & H. 19977

267 [lsmrd]

drmdms | d d | lsmdls | r r | rrmdr | drmdms | d d

268

s s | m | s s | r | msmr | d m | slmr | d m | slmr | d

269

m r | mrdr | m d | s r | mrdr | m d | s s | slmr | m d | r l | slmr | d d

270

s m | s m | smr | m | s m | s m | smr | d

r r r r | r s m | l l l l | l | s m | s m | s m | smr | d

271

drmr | d s | l d | m s | l l | s | msls | m r | d s | m l | m r | d

278 `lsmrdl,`

2/4 l m | r r s | l m | r r d | d r m m | s m r d | m r | l, l, l, ‖

279

2/4 l, l, r r | d r l, :‖ l l l l | s s s s | l l m m | r r r ᵧ ‖

280

2/4 l, d | r d r | l, | m s | l s l | m | m s | l s m r | m d | r d r | l, ‖

281

2/4 l m | l s m | r m d r | m | r s | m d | r d m r | l, ‖

282

2/4 m r | m d l, | l s | l m r | s s s s | s m r d | r d | l, l, l, ‖

283

2/4 m m l | s s l | m r s | d d r | m r m | l, l, d | r d r | l, l, l, ‖

B. & H. 19977

288 `lsmrdl,`
2/4

m m l l | l s m | r m s m | r m d | m l | r m d | d r m r | l, l, l, ‖

289
2/4

l m l | l m l | s l s m | r r | m d m l | s d | r m r d | l, l, ‖

290
2/4

l m l s | m r | m d m r | d l, | d r m | s m r | m d m r | l, l, ‖

291
2/4

m s l s | m s l | m s l s | m r d | l, d r d | l, d r | m s m r | l, l, l, ‖

292
2/4

l, d l, d | l, d m | r m d l, | d l, l, | l, d l, d | l, d m | r m d l, | d l, l, |

l l | s r s | l m m r | m m m | l, d l, d | l, d m | r m d l, | d l, l, ‖

298 | lsmrdl₁ |

d l₁ d r | m s m m | l s m d | m r l₁ l₁ ‖

299

m r m l₁ | d r l₁ l₁

l s l m | s l m m | l s l m | s m d r | m l₁ m r | d r l₁ l₁ ‖

300 | smrdl₁s₁ |

d d s₁ s₁ | d r m | r d r d | s₁ s₁ ‖ s m m | m r d |

r m r d | r r | s m m | m r d | r m r d | s₁ s₁ ‖

301

s₁ s₁ | s s | s r | m d ‖ r d | l₁ l₁ | d d | m r | m d | l₁ l₁ | l₁ r | d s₁ ‖

302

l₁ m | r m | s m r | m ‖ r r r m | d l₁ | d d r | m ‖ d l₁ s₁ | l₁ ‖

54

319
l s m r d l, s,
l l m m s m r s l l m m s m r m r r l, l, d l, s, d
r r l, l, d l, s, l,
320
l, d l, d l, d r r d l, s, l, l, l, m s m s
m s l l s m r m m m m m d l, d l, d l, d r r d l, s, l, l, l,
321
s m r d r m s l m r d r m d l, s, l, d r m d l, s,
322
s, s, s s l s r m r d s r m r d l, s, s, d s, s, s,

58

327 `r'd'lsmrd`

d' d l s | m d r r | d' d l s | m r d d | r s l s | l d' s s | r' d' s m | l s d d ‖

328 `m'r'd'lsr`

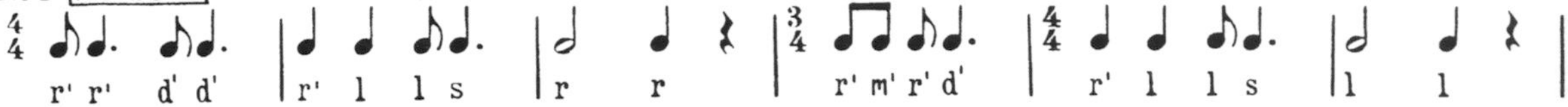

r' r' d' d' | r' l l s | r r | r' m' r' d' | r' l l s | l l

r' m' r' d' | r' l l s | l r | s s d' d' | r' l l s | r r ‖

329 `m'r'd'lsrd`

r' r' l l | r' r' | d' r' m' d' | r' l | s s d' r' | d' l | s l s d | r r

330

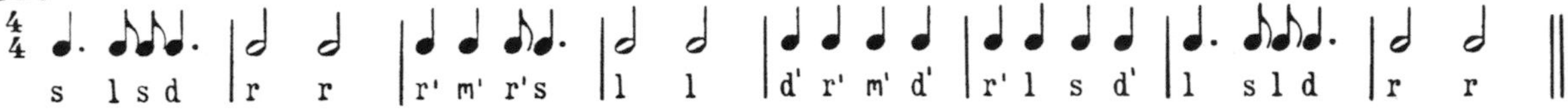

s l s d | r r | r' m' r's | l l | d' r' m' d' | r' l s d' | l s l d | r r ‖

B.& H.19977

Printed by
Halstan & Co. Ltd., Amersham, Bucks., England

Old Man

Hounds never burned up a country as did the Millbeck hounds that day.

See page 9

OLD MAN

And Other
Colonel Weatherford Stories

by

GORDON GRAND

Paintings by William J. Hays

THE DERRYDALE PRESS

LANHAM AND NEW YORK

THE DERRYDALE PRESS

Published in the United States of America
by The Derrydale Press
4720 Boston Way, Lanham, Maryland 20706

Distributed by NATIONAL BOOK NETWORK, INC.

Original Derrydale printing 1934
First paperback printing with french folds 2000

ISBN 1-56833-143-6 (pbk. : alk. paper)

⊖™The paper used in this publication meets the minimum requirements of
American National Standard for Information Sciences—Permanence of
Paper for Printed Library Materials, ANSI/NISO Z39.48-1992.
Manufactured in the United States of America.

To

My Little Daughter

H E L E N

Who says of Fox Hunting as do the

Hungarians of their native land:

Extra Hungarian non est vita

vel si quidem est, non est ita.

PUBLISHER'S NOTE

The publisher intended to issue this book with illustrations by J. Alden Twachtman, whose drawings appeared in the author's companion volumes.

A decision, recently reached, to bring the book out in the autumn rather than next spring, unhappily precluded the possibility of Colonel Twachtman illustrating the text due to the shortness of time available.

In this emergency Mr. William J. Hays, a friend and neighbor of the author at Millbrook, New York, generously loaned his canvases of the Millbrook Hunt, depicting scenes around which Mr. Grand's stories are written.

While the plates were in preparation Mr. Hays died. The five pictures appearing in this volume were his last canvases of a country across which he hunted for twenty years.

E. V. C.

Contents

Illustrations

Old Man

CHAPTER I.

Old Man

We dropped heavily into Colonel Weatherford's copious leather arm chairs and awaited tea, the sequel to a long, wearing fox hunting day.

The warmth of the fire-lit library after so many hours afield must have made me drowsy, for sounds and movements were as things dreamed. Then I heard the Colonel's voice coming to me as from a great distance. "Pendleton, I have just learned that Algerton Le Courte has been awarded the Victoria Cross for an act of supreme courage out in India."

The mention of a name which had long since dropped from my memory recalled tales of a little English boy who had once tarried in our village for a few years and then journeyed on. I never knew him, but in the passage of time I read of his riding races and hunting hounds in England, and once of his piloting his horse to the victory of victories over the bleak, foreboding Grand National course, with the dour, wind-swept land enveloped in mist and rain. And again I read of him at Gallipoli in the Great War.

To me he was but a legend or as a knight in an old wives' tale. If his name was mentioned a soft, warm, pensive look stole over women's faces as though they took some pleasant memory to their hearts; and he but just a little boy. "Colonel Weatherford," I said, "tell me. Who was Algerton Le Courte?"

The Colonel sat smoking his pipe and gazing into the fire for some time. "Well, Pendleton," he said, "I never quite knew why General Le Courte and his small son came here to Millbeck. They arrived from England one Spring morning accompanied by a family retainer, old Middleton, an excellent servant, and rented the Rose Cottage on Highminster. As soon as they were settled I called to pay my respects to the old General." Colonel Weatherford lapsed into silence, groping in the archives of memory for those word pictures that would best describe his old and valued friend. "Pendleton," he continued, "have you read The Newcomes?" "Yes," I answered. "Well, General Le Courte was made very much in the mold of Colonel Newcome — a quiet, dignified, somewhat old-fashioned gentleman, but Pendleton, a great gentleman, a naturalist, a fine sportsman, and a soldier who had carried on for England in all her hinterlands.

"In a year or two the son entered the Millbeck Academy as a day pupil, and every morning the General would drive him to school in a Mineola cart behind an old-fashioned, smart-moving cob he had picked up some place for a song. I would often meet them bumping over the rough, back country roads as I started off with hounds. They were sufficient unto themselves, those two, and inseparable.

"As time went on the General and I became fast friends. We shot and fished together, and I enjoyed his comments on passing events and the worthwhile books of the day. After some years of this companionship a slow, stealthy change commenced creeping over the General, creeping so slowly at first that it was hardly discernible. He started missing birds he had no right to miss, then making excuses why he could not go shooting. One day, while fishing, he experienced no end of difficulty tying on his flies, and requested my help. If I asked him whether he thought well of a certain book I had loaned him he became evasive and pleaded lack of opportunity to read. In time he gave up driving the Mineola cart and sat as a passenger while old Middleton did the driving. I did not piece two and two together until one day when visiting him I noticed him walk over to the table for a match. The match box was in plain sight but I saw him feeling vaguely for it along the table. He put the matches in his pocket and left the room. When he returned his pipe was going. On a sweet, gentle day in mid-June the last flickering rays of light receded and left him in eternal darkness.

"With a desire to alleviate some of the loneliness, I now saw more of both father and son. Shut off from other contacts and activities the General's thoughts reverted more and more to the boy, his education and future. He wanted him to play at all games and learn of all sports, and his interest and curiosity in the youngster's progress was insatiable. I would now and again take the boy shooting, and the old General would persist in coming along, with Middleton to lead him. If game fell to the boy's gun the father must needs know the length of the shot, was the bird well hit, was it rocketing high overhead or flying low, an in-comer or going away from him; was the boy's stance as it should have been, etc., etc. I can still hear him saying, 'Tell me, Weatherford, did the Old Man do well?' He practically never referred to the boy except as Old Man.

[3]

"Pendleton, if you look at the eyes of any noteworthy sportsman who has excelled both in sports and in the playing of games you will read much of the causes of those successes. This boy had just such eyes, and fair hair, fine, true Anglo-Saxon features, and a smile that made you want to go up and put your arm around his shoulder.

"In time he took to playing football and was considered the fastest-running and hardest line-hitting back who ever played for our little pre-preparatory school. Every Fall afternoon the General would have Middleton drive him to the football field. They would poke the pony close up to the side lines and the General would question Middleton, to whom the game was a complete enigma, as to what Old Man was doing now. Had he carried the ball in the last play — how many yards had he made? I once stood by the cart when Middleton was trying to describe a play, 'One of the young gentlemen handed the ball to Master Algy, sir, and Master Algy attempted to pass right up the meadow with it. I'm sure he had every intention of doing so, sir, but some of the other young gentlemen got quite in his way, and in the disturbance he was knocked down, sir, and a number of young gentlemen fell on him. I don't think he is harmed, sir, only a trifle soiled. I could brush him off directly, sir, if you wish.'

"During the principal game of the year I sat on a rug with the General out in front of the players' benches. It was the day of our school's supreme effort. The score stood nothing to nothing. There was but five minutes left to play. We had the ball. The signal rang out clear and sharp. It was the Old Man's signal, and the ball was passed to him. He found or made an opening and went through. Boy after boy dove for him and tried for him. On and on he went. Only two players stood between him and the goal and victory. They both tried for him and missed: eighty yards for a winning touchdown. I depicted every move to the blind old warrior beside me. God, Pendleton, the look on the man's face. Automobile horns were screaming all over the place. Every Millbeck boy was on his feet. The cheer leaders jumped to their positions. 'A Millbeck School cheer for Le Courte — everybody in it. Are you ready? One, two, three — Millbeck, Millbeck, Millbeck, Le Courte, Le Courte, Le Courte.'

"Pendleton, I suppose I'm what's known as a crusty, worldly, sophisticated old bachelor, but I am still affected by the picture of the General noiselessly clapping the palm of one hand against the back of the other, not the two palms together. No, no. There must be no noise, no display, no sign of emotion, just clapping gently and saying softly. 'First rate, Old Man, first rate!'

"But the General laid the most stress of all upon the Old Man's riding. He had sold his Purdey gun and put the proceeds into a smart, weedy little thoroughbred horse for the boy. The thing was not much to look at and had very little in the way of manners, but it could positively fly and jump like a disorganized rocket.

"The General had been considered one of the crack horsemen of England, and he tried — tried so hard and so long — to form a satisfactory mental picture of the boy's riding, of his seat and hands and horsemanship.

"I once drove the father in the old pony cart to the very top of Pugsley Hill on a day when his boy was hunting, in the hope that he might hear the cry of hounds and the thud of galloping horses.

"It was a warm, fair morning in Indian Summer. We sat

[5]

in the cart, I smoking and he pulling on his now ever empty pipe while the pony cropped the grass. I had instructed Will Madden, the Huntsman, to draw Peckett's Woods from the north and work on down towards us. As we listened the faint note of the horn would now and again come to us and drift gently by to be lost in the vastness of Malvern Swamp. Suddenly hounds unkenneled their fox. Peckett's Woods awoke. The eager, clamorous cry rolled up towards us, one bellow of sound pressing the one in front until Great Pugsley was enveloped in music — the bass notes of the old dog hounds, the altos and sopranos of the keen, active, flying bitches.

"I stood up in the cart. They were racing towards us. 'Look sharp, Weatherford,' called the General. 'Look sharp, old man. You will view the fox. Keep your eyes down wind.'

" 'Tally-ho, General. Tally-ho. There he romps,' I sang out. God, Pendleton, but he was a big, strong rover. On came the dull, persisting thud of horses' hoofs. 'Steady boy, steady on,' I called to the pony, and took him by the head.

" 'Can you see them, Weatherford? Can you see them yet?'

" 'Yes, yes, General. They are heading for the great wall into Malvern lane. Here they come. Will Madden is safe over.'

" 'Where is my Old Man, Weatherford? Is he well up with the first flight? Is he over yet? Tell, me, has he a nice light, airy seat? He is not away back in the ruck, is he, Colonel, not milling around with the tail-enders?' 'No, no, General,' I told him. 'He is well over, well over, going brilliantly, magnificently. He is taking his own line. They are turning south straight into the sun and galloping towards the post-and-rail fence with the big drop into Westmoreland Bottom. They are riding too fast. It's a terrible drop. There he is, there he is. There is the Old Man. God bless me, what a jump his horse made. He flew it in his stride and landed going away.'

"They passed from view and were engulfed in the endless swales and woods and uplands that stretch on and on to where even enduring hounds may not explore. Nothing told of their passing beyond a faint suspended cloud of dust over Wendover pastures, and a lone, riderless horse cantering uncertainly in the valley below us.

"But that which touched us closer than all else was the devotion of the boy to his father. No one who lived in Millbeck in those days will ever forget that picture. It was many years later and long after he had left us that I finally evolved the true significance of the boy's character and ideals. Pride of race and background and of one's forebears and their achievements are sometimes very dominant incentives. I would now and again catch the son looking at the blind father. At such moments the boy's forehead would be creased with lines of perplexity and rebellion at so cruel a visitation, but creased too with a great determination to do his part, to live up to all that was expected of him. That was to be his contribution. At such moments the lines about his mouth depicted the things of the spirit.

"The English historian, Trevelyan, described in telling words the charge of the perfectly trained and brilliantly accoutred British troops marching in perfect alignment with steady tramp up the slope of Bunker Hill to be mowed down by skilled marksmen behind embankments. As the front line fell other British troops stepped over them, took their place, and marched gallantly on in the same perfect alignment. The order had been, forward. There were no questions asked.

[7]

The order had simply been forward on. It was thus Algerton Le Courte marched on. He was gay and playful in his marching, but he had no thought of turning back. With him to give but part of what one had to give, whether it be on the playing field, in the stubble, across country, or in the class-room, would have been as halting on Bunker Hill. His father would not have thought well of that. That's why, Pendleton, you have read of him winning races and hunting hounds in England and facing the Turks at Gallipoli, and why he now wears the Victoria Cross.

"It came on to the Saturday of our cup race. (It was the year my horse, The Woldsman, ran third). It was a wicked day — wind in the northeast and a cold slashing rain. The General would not move about but sat huddled up in the pony cart. He caught cold. Monday night pneumonia set in. On Friday another English gentleman reported *adsum*. That evening I brought Old Man over here to stay with me.

"The services were set for Sunday. We discussed at some length whether to take hounds out on Saturday, and finally decided to do so informally, the members to ride in mufti. The General was not a landowner or subscriber, nor did he hunt himself, and would have been the last to have wanted hounds kept in kennels on his account. Certainly not with the countryside full of visitors.

"Henry Newcombe was Master that year but was away, and I had promised to take the field. As I left the kennels I was surprised and a trifle annoyed to see the Old Man riding up the road. His training should have suggested the impropriety of such an act, even to a boy of fourteen. The thought struck me that if his horse needed exercise he could very easily have found someone to exercise it for him, or at least he could have ridden in some less conspicuous place than around the kennels. And so I dismissed the matter."

The Colonel paused, re-lit his pipe, then looked over at me. "Pendleton, a pack of hounds never burned up a country as the Millbeck hounds burned this country up that day. We met at Upper Stanfordville Bridge away over to the north-west.

"Towards late afternoon Will Madden took hounds in to the Oak Spring woods, entering from the north. We had not been in covert over a minute or two when I heard halloing from down at the southeast corner. A hound opened and almost instantly the entire pack boiled out of covert. The scent must have been very unusual that day, for I have seldom seen hounds tumble out of woods with such drive and cry. George Ashley had viewed the fox away and told me he was an exceptionally big, strong-running old customer that had set his head straight for Oaklands.

"The fox sank the hill down to Foster's Creek, crossed, went away towards Round Top, which he skirted to the west, then on for Oaklands, as the crow flies. I was splashing through the creek when I heard a horse crossing somewhat below me — crossing wide open, fairly rocketing along, and bless my soul if it wasn't Old Man on that Flying Spinnaker of his.

"Pendleton, I'm not possessed of the best temper in the world, and the very sight of the boy hunting on such a day angered me beyond all reason — the heartlessness of the thing — the indifference. Will Madden was just in front of me. I called out to him to catch the boy and send him back to me. Will was mounted on a thoroughbred horse called Acclaim, by Plaudit. He had won some good races and could

fly. Will set sail. Pendleton, he might just as well have
chased a rainbow, for by this time the Old Man was the
length of Peckett's meadow ahead of us and right on the tail
of hounds. Foot is indispensable in a good hunter, but God
bless me, there is a pace beyond which no sane man will cross
a country. That boy was not riding as a sane person should,
and hounds were not running as hounds generally run.

"When we reached Trimble Uplands, close by Oaklands
Village, I had a magnificent view. Hounds were tightly
packed and fairly driving and pulling each other along, the
scent stinging their noses. The Old Man was still on their
tails, but Will Madden was two fields behind him, yet riding
as few men have ever ridden that country.

"From Oaklands the fox set his head for the Skittles,
crossing Jobe Hecker's, Peckham's and Ed Simpson's farms.
There was no wire in those days, and chestnut posts and rails
were still available. God bless me, but it took a good horse
to cross that country. Luck was with me crossing Hecker's
farm for I hazarded a guess that the line would bend south,
so skirted the hill, and by so doing nicked in with Madden.
His horse looked as though he had been through the mill.
When we finally worked our way out of Peckham's peach
orchard we saw hounds streaming across the sheep downs beyond on Simpson's farm, and Old Man snuggled right up
with them. Dear old Mrs. Estey was out that day. She knew
what was going on in my mind and shoved her horse up to
me. I can hear her now, saying, 'Colonel, he is only a little
boy. We must not be too hard on him. Promise me you won't.
He is magnificent.' I suppose I simply grunted at her, but
God bless me, my indignation at the boy knew no bounds.
We galloped on and on across those far reaches of our north

country crowding and taxing our horses, grimly pursuing a fair-haired boy and a streaming, flying pack of hounds.

"By the time we reached the foot of the Skittles most of the field had dropped by the wayside, for we had been running close to an hour without a breather. I had sent my second horse home earlier in the day, and The Woldsman was discouraged at the two hundred pounds he had been lugging at such a pace.

"Due to the light having become exceedingly bad Will Madden's horse, which Will always let step on to his fences too fast, had brought himself up under a big, upstanding post-and-rail fence and turned Will over with a wicked thud. My horse started to jump, found himself in wrong, tried to stop, and slid into the fence, hitting it with his head and off shoulder. He sprawled about but finally lurched up on his legs. Darkness had defeated us. We could go no further. A fence too treacherous and formidable to be jumped in such light stood before us. The members of the field drifted homeward while Will Madden, the Huntsman, and I waited alone in the growing dusk listening.

"Suddenly the hunted line turned and led towards us and the eager, pressing cry became clearer. Then silence settled over all the land. Hounds had lost. They had over-run their line. 'Blow, Will,' I called. 'Quick, man, blow. Blow hounds to us. Call them before they find again.' Will stood up in his stirrups and blew until the hills echoed. We harked. Only Woodsman's daughter, little Fantasy, came to the horn and she falteringly, reluctant, and of two minds. Then from a swale of land at the fringe of the twilight a boy's voice drifted faintly to us. 'Come, come, come — come-ee lads, come, come, come.' He was imitating old Madden, and calling hounds to him. Again the cry of hounds. He had cast them, found the line and they were driving on in the dusk.

"Pendleton, at that moment I could have thrashed the boy, young as he was. The recklessness of the thing, the abandon, the infernal determination of youth for self-assertiveness, and worse, Pendleton, the untimeliness, the impropriety of his riding and playing on such a day; a day on which many had given up their sport out of respect for his father.

"We finally located the road which runs down to Black Tim's Anvil, at Merrittsville, and rode along, harking as we went, but by then the land was quiet as a tomb. When we came to Ed Holcombe's, Ed was standing on his front porch looking into the darkness. I rode in and asked him if he had heard hounds. 'Listen,' he said, and from the hills, far, far to the north, came the distant cry, as faint as a dying note of music. There was no possible chance of our getting to them so we went on towards Merrittsville, blowing from time to time. We stopped at the church this side of the village, but only the far away barking of a house dog and a horse's hoofs on a distant road disturbed the stillness. It would be hard to depict Will Madden's feeling as we stood in the darkening shadow of that old church. I can hear him now. 'Hounds be tired, sir, and the fox be tired. They don't be runnin' him like afore. Do you know what Master Algy be a doin' sir? He be leadin' over the fences — jumpin' on and off and leadin' over. That little, old, wizened up horse is a followin' of him like a dog out there in the dark. Leadin' over out there in the dark. It be rough out there, sir. I mind that patch of country. It be mostly slash and rocks and stone walls. He, out there with my hounds in the dark, and me a standin' at this here church.'

[12]

"We passed through the village of Merrittsville and heard hounds when we were close to Black Tim's Anvil, and once again a mile beyond, and that was the last we heard of them.

"We poked about here and there in the dark harking, blowing, and asking, but apparently the fox had run steadily away from us. Concluding at last that whatever might have happened, hounds were probably now headed for home, we jogged along over a rough, stony, rutty road, with here and there deep puddles over the surface of which thin skims of ice were forming. It's twelve miles from Merrittsville to the kennels.

"When we came into Bangdollen they told us that hounds were on the road some distance in front of us with a young boy. A man standing by the roadside said, 'and he ha a fox wee him. I see it.' As we jogged on an old couplet came to me,

'*A hundred horsemen saw him found;*
How many saw him die?'

"I am not proud of my part that night. When we came up with the hounds I asked Old Man if he was all right, for I was deeply concerned; then we rode on together saying little, for I was out of tune with the boy. But when we reached the house and were about to dismount I felt that I could not properly drop the subject of his hunting without some comment, so I said, 'Old Man, I am a bit surprised, perhaps just a bit disappointed about your having been out today.' 'Sorry, sir,' was all he answered, and turned towards the house.

"He sent down word by my man that if I would excuse him he would like to have dinner in his room. I dined alone, tormented beyond words at the thought of the boy being by himself on such a night. After dinner I started up to see him, but not wishing to intrude, finally sent the man up to say that I would very much like to sit with him a while either in the library or in his room. He again asked to be excused on the ground that he was tired and had turned in. I tried to read, tried to write, tried thumbing the piano, tried everything. God bless me, but I was upset, and wished I had never taken hounds out. Being tuckered I at length turned in but could not sleep, so crept upstairs to see if by any chance the boy was still awake. The room was in darkness and the door locked.

"I don't know how long I had been asleep or what time it might have been when suddenly I was conscious of someone tapping on the door. I sat up, turned on the night light, and called, 'Come in.'

"He had on a blue bath robe, one sleeve of which was empty. He walked to the foot of the bed, stood up very straight, looked squarely at me, and said, 'I'm very sorry, Sir, to have wakened you. I couldn't help it, Sir. I had to. I couldn't stand it any longer, Sir. I can't have you disappointed in me. Dad wouldn't like it. You were very good to him, Sir. I'm sorry, but I had to hunt today.'

"I did not answer him for a moment, determined to think twice before speaking. The boy's appearance alarmed me. He was but fourteen years old, yet as he stood there he might have been of middle age. The constant, haunting thoughts and remembrances of the father lying at the little home on Highminster were tormenting the boy beyond all endurance. From his position I knew that either his shoulder or collar bone was broken, and had now been broken for many hours. 'Old Man,' I said, 'we won't talk about your having hunted today. I shall never refer to it again or think about it, and don't you think about it.'

"The boy took hold of the foot of the bed with his good hand. I could see the knuckles growing white with the intensity of his grip. 'You still don't understand, Sir. Can't you see, Sir? Can't you understand? I should think *you* could understand, Sir,' and there was a note of impatience in the tense, trembling voice. He left the foot of the bed and came close to me. His hand was working convulsively. 'Don't you see, Sir — it was the first time, the only time, he has ever been able to see me ride to hounds. He had been waiting a long time, Sir. I couldn't keep him waiting. It had been a long time, Sir.' He turned, went out of the room, and closed the door very softly. As I reached for the telephone I heard him passing hesitatingly down the hall.

CHAPTER II.

Thamis McWuthey

From my farm to the village of Millbeck is a matter of some five miles, but half way between the two lies Marysville, at the junction of an important north and south country road. Unless you were in need of gas or perhaps seeking the way you would be apt to slip entirely through Marysville unconscious of its importance, and probably oblivious to Mr. Thomas Ashby's general store.

For close to forty years Thomas Ashby had conducted this store, serving his neighbors cheerily and honorably, until the failing health of Mrs. Ashby caused him to put the property on the market in order to take his wife to a more lenient climate. If you have ever lived in a quiet, remote farming district where the friendliness and helpfulness of neighbors is of moment you will appreciate that our interest in Mr. Ashby's successor was more than academic.

I was sitting in my car in front of the post office one early spring day when down the road came my old friend and neighbor, Colonel John Weatherford, in his Lancia runabout. Seeing me he pulled to the side of the road, stopped, came over, squeezed his huge frame into my car, and slammed the door, all without saying good morning or how do you do.

"Now, then, Pendleton," he commenced, "God bless me,

what's this about Ashby having sold his store to Salvatore Salvato?" I don't remember my reply, which is perhaps just as well.

A few years back the name of this Salvatore Salvato, alias "The Gas House Terror," had commenced creeping into the sporting pages. Piloted by a skillful manager adept at discovering soft berths and gaining publicity, this formidably set up son of Italy had made a slight stir in pugilistic circles. He had fought a galaxy of third-raters, talked large himself and paid others to talk equally large about him, until by reason of too much talking his physical well-being was placed in jeopardy for he was faced with the necessity of meeting an exceedingly hard-hitting opponent. Thereupon Salvato, product of a decadent age of the noble science, retired from the ring. Urged on by a relative, who unhappily for us lived in Millbeck, the erstwhile pugilist negotiated the purchase of Thomas Ashby's store, encouraged by the prospect of becoming a large frog in our rural puddle.

The Marysville general store, specimen of a fine American institution and honorable and respected for close to a hundred years, underwent immediate and radical changes. The stock room at the rear of the store soon housed a pool table. The less steady of our employees took to dropping in at Salvato's and drifting home from thence the worse for wear; the place became a pest to the countryside at large.

A greater braggart and bully never lived than this same Salvatore Salvato. True he cast a spell upon a certain class of people, for ours is a very quiet countryside, few heroes appearing in it. This man's former contacts with the great and near great in sportdom, coupled with his braggadocio in depicting these contacts and the part he had played in this tawdry realm of sport, formed a highly seasoned diet for a rural audience. As a final protest against Salvato's management some of us withdrew our patronage, a gesture which had small economic effect on the proprietor, for Dutchess County "apple" is more profitable than flour.

Matters went from bad to worse until two events happened which tended to focus public attention on the situation.

Among Colonel Weatherford's domestic staff was a Scotchman by the name of John McGregor, a somewhat pathetic character generally referred to as the "handy boy,"— although probably a less handy individual never entered domestic service. McGregor's father had long served the Colonel's family as gardener, and the Colonel for sentimental reasons had installed the son in his household and kept an eye on him. A more harmless individual never lived. Some infantile illness had left the boy an anemic weakling, incapable of doing heavy work; but he performed his few simple duties with the greatest pride and exactness. His entire existence appeared to be centered in and about Colonel Weatherford.

On a Saturday night in early summer McGregor was returning from the village with Eddie Walsh, one of the Colonel's grooms. Walsh stopped the car at Salvato's, set upon looking things over, as he said. McGregor declined to enter the place, but after waiting a reasonable time went in search of Walsh, with the intent of persuading him to come home. Just what happened within the store is somewhat shrouded in mystery, but it appeared that Salvato had been drinking heavily, and upon seeing McGregor he indulged in some very derogatory remarks concerning Colonel Weatherford. Little McGregor, trembling with indignation, then and there gave the prize fighter what is generally considered to have been the most versatile and exhaustive tongue-lashing ever heard within the confines of Dutchess County.

As soon as Salvato, to whom such a thing had never happened before, could recover from his astonishment, he delivered so brutal a blow upon McGregor's frail person as to cause him to be confined in the hospital for some three weeks, not so much from the blow itself but rather from the after effects, for McGregor's nervous system seemed to have been completely shattered. The Colonel took the affair very much to heart and served notice upon his employees that if one of them ever entered Salvato's place he would be discharged forthwith. There was little more he could do, for it was conceded that McGregor's remarks were rather more pointed than a proprietor could be expected to subscribe to. On the other hand there was no possible justification for an experienced, hard-hitting professional to man-handle so ruthlessly and brutally a sickly individual of half his size.

With the effects of McGregor's combat still irritating us another situation developed which aroused even those far removed from contacts with Marysville or its store. We had at that time as second Whipper-in to our hounds a splendid southern boy, Carter Wheatly, of whom the entire countryside, particularly the fox hunting fraternity, thought very highly. He was a finished horseman, kindly, patient, and sympathetic with horses and hounds, and a great favorite. In the course of events his quiet southern voice and noticeable good looks made themselves felt in the village, and it became rumored that he was in high favor with little Ruth Faulkner, who was quite a reigning beauty.

Personally I have never been able to subscribe to the old

adage that all the world loves a lover. I should rather think the reverse might be more true, but nevertheless, seeing Carter and his lady love together one day walking down the opposite side of the street, Colonel Weatherford fumbled around for his glasses and stood on the curb watching the pair as long as they were in sight, then turned to me, saying, "Well, God bless my soul, Pendleton, I had forgotten all about such things. Bless me but they are a good-looking young couple." We started down towards the bank when suddenly the Colonel pulled up short, "Now, then, now, then, where are they going to live?" he inquired. "Carter can't live in the village. He must be up near the kennels." I ventured the opinion that the Colonel's deductions might be a bit premature, "Not a bit of it, Pendleton," he replied, "not a bit. We must help an affair of that kind along. That's all we're good for when we get old." And he stood pondering upon the matter. Then, looking up, he saw George Whalling, our expert on all real estate matters, and called him over. "George," he said, "what about that cottage half a mile up the roads from the kennels? Who owns it? Is it for sale? What's it worth? Could it be made habitable?" Whalling told him it belonged to old man Sanford, was in fair repair, and could be bought for eighteen hundred dollars. "All right," said the Colonel, "go and buy it. Buy it as close as you can, and telephone Eben Makepiece to inspect the place and send me an estimate for fixing it up."

This little incident served to put a domineering and quite crochety old bachelor in the way of discovering that he had preserved a modicum of romance. From having instructed the carpenter, plumber, electrician and all others performing work on the cottage to do a modest job with a constant eye to the pennies, the Colonel became more and more expansive and increasingly secretive. It was Eben Makepiece, the carpenter, who enlightened me by asking, "Whatever is the Colonel planning to do with that cottage of old man Sanford's? I never see the like of the way he's carryin' on. A blue bath tub, fancy copper sink, and all such notions. He comes ridin' by this mornin' and asks me to hold his horse while he looks around. When he comes out he says, 'God bless my soul, Eben, isn't there a chimney and open fire in that living room?' 'No,' I tells him. 'Well, build one,' he says."

Eben Makepiece is a staunch Presbyterian, and any Sunday morning you can see him stumping down the aisle of the confederated church with the collection basket. He finally turned to me with that grave, solemn face of his even graver than usual, "Mr. Pendleton, you wouldn't be thinkin' maybe the Colonel was fixin' up old man Sanford's cottage for a purpose you and me wouldn't be minded to mention, would you?" I set his mind at rest.

The quiet, droning days of summer finally gave way to early Autumn. Our fox hunting season opens on the first Saturday in October, on which day the entire countryside assembles at George Osborne's cross roads. We come on foot, on bicycles, in cars, or mounted on our favorite horses. As I rode down the side of the State road that morning on Jack Semple, little Ruth Faulkner came speeding past me in an ancient, rickety car to have a look at her Lochinvar emblazed in coat of hunting pink and velvet cap.

I would not belittle the dangers incurred by our valiant air mail pilots as they rove the heavens or the hazards of riveters balancing on slender beams sixty stories skyward, but perhaps there is no class of men who are so continuously exposed

to danger and hard knocks as Whippers-in to a fast pack of
fox hounds hunting a formidable country. Falls are inevitable, and a fall harder than the last is always in the offing.

The accident happened as we raced down from Hatcher's
Hill. The breast-high scent was pungent and propelling.
Hounds fairly boiled along with their eager clamorous cry
welling up to us in ever increasing volume. Half way down
the hill, dividing the Hatcher and Benham lands, stands a
great grey eighteenth century wall, built in the days when
oxen labored. And since that wall was built generations of
Hatchers and Benhams have hauled fresh crops of stones and
piled them at the bottom or on the top of this ancestral boundary. And so we raced on down to the grim, grey obstacle
each selecting a favored spot for his horse to jump. Will
Madden, the Huntsman, on Timemaster, was a few strides
in the lead. Off to his left rode Colonel Weatherford, the
Master of Hounds, going great guns, and far over to the
right I saw the slim, graceful figure of Carter Wheatly riding down to that great wall on his horse, Master of the
Marches,— riding in that gay, gallant, forward way of his.
We were going too fast, all of us, and we knew it. I was in
mid-air when I saw the boy fall. They came down together,
but the Master of the Marches was on top. As I landed I
swung my mount right-handed and galloped to him. His
horse, dazed and shaking, was scrambling to his feet, leaving the boy a limp, crumpled, broken thing.

I don't know where she came from, or how, but when I
had fearfully turned him over and was struggling with the
gold safety pin that held his white hunting stock, a soft, fal-
tering little voice said, "Please let me try, Mr. Pendleton."

Dick Estey and I left her holding the boy's head on her

[23]

lap, looking down at a white, drawn face, and gently brushing the hair back from his forehead. She was quiet and reserved in all she said and did, but the haunting fear and dread in her eyes made me turn away. Estey and I unhinged a door from Ed Hatcher's barn and carried him out to the road, lifted him into the car and they took him home.

We worried along through the balance of that hunting season without a second Whipper-in, while Carter Wheatly gazed longingly out of a hospital window. The boy had spent his life afield. He knew and loved the glory of autumn with its panoply of succeeding colours—the swamp maples, sumac on the uplands, followed by the shimmering gold on hardwood ridges, and at winter's coming the somber browns of the persisting oak leaves.

The Hunt fixture card, a constant reminder of all he yearned for, showing where hounds were to meet, was tacked on the wall at his bedside. "Monday, October sixth, at Smithboro Church. Wednesday, at Turkey Hollow Ford. Friday, at Fenwick Corners. Saturday, at Bangdall School House," —and so on through the weeks and months.

The nurses were helpless, the doctors distracted. They said he needed absolute quiet and mental rest. His brain must not be stimulated. He must not talk or be talked to. But he would not rest. Orders pertaining to his own welfare meant naught to him, for he was a true son of Virginia. "They are just moving off from Smithboro church, mam," he would say to the nurse. "It's five minutes past nine. They will be drawing Baggett's covert first, mam. I reckon Will Madden, he's our Huntsman, will be riding old Timemaster. Tim O'Conner will be on that Sliding Sue mare. Colonel Weatherford, the Master, will be up on Kerry's Own, 'cause it's our Smithboro

At the foot of Smithboro Hill

country — that's our biggest country, mam. They'll be 'most up to Baggett's by now. Somebody will be letting down the bar-way — maybe some kid who didn't go to school so as he could see hounds meet. I used to do that, mam. I reckon they are just pushing through the bar-way now.

"It's our bitch pack we hunt today, mam. Tim O'Conner, the first Whip, will be pulling up the west side of the covert. If I was there, mam, I'd be riding Atkinson. He's by Jack Atkin, and him and me would be pullin' up the east side. Do you know where I stand, mam, when they draw Baggett's covert? Clean on the top of Smithboro Hill. That's where I stand. A fox can't break from Baggett's to the east without me viewing him away. You never heard me halloa a fox away from covert, did you mam? I sure wish I were up on Smithboro now. Please, mam, what time would it be? I wonder did they find in Baggett's. Maybe Mr. Pendleton took my place and went up the east side of the covert. Would you think maybe they found, mam? You'd like those bitches, mam. They hunt powerful sharp. I wish sometime you could hear them. Why, mam, when scenting is good and they come out of covert together you'd think it was a choir singing at Easter time. Maybe some day when I get fixed up you could come over to Millbeck and see those bitches and the dog pack and the horses I ride, Atkinson, Master of the Marches, he's the one let me down — he's the best one, and Maid-in-Waiting. She's by Bachelor, out of Wedding Bells, by Chimes of Athol.

"Please, mam, I don't want any more of that medicine. Do I have to take it? It makes me sleepy so I can't think of the Hunt or anything. Would you mind telling me, mam, whether a lady has been here yet this morning, the one that was here yesterday? You wouldn't know whether she came alone yesterday, would you, mam? You didn't see anybody with her yesterday — not an Italian — a big Italian with a scar? You'd have known whether the Italian came with her, wouldn't you, mam? Maybe you would have been looking out of the window and seen them. She don't want him to come with her, mam, only he won't leave her alone. You'd think her people would help her, only they don't, 'cause the Italian has a power of money. Please, mam, if you see that Italian bringing her to the hospital to see me you'll tell me.

"If Master of the Marches were my horse I would like for you to hunt him some day — some day when we had found in Wendover bottom and gone away south to Pugsley Hill. That's a fine bit of grass land to gallop across and there are a pile of big fences up at Pugsley. You'd like those big fences, mam, and you'd be surprised how the Master of the Marches steps down to his fences. He sails them wide open. I sure wish you could ride him to make up for all the trouble I'm making for you. Do I have to go to sleep now? If that lady comes you'll let me know, won't you, mam, and maybe while I'm sleeping you won't be so busy and could look out the window and see if that big Italian is driving her. Goodbye mam. I wish I knew whether they found a fox in Baggett's covert."

He came back to Millbeck from the hospital on an afternoon in early December, white, frail-looking, with a permanent limp and one shoulder lower than the other. I went into town and brought him out and took little Ruth Faulkner with me.

What it was he heard that afternoon after I brought him home — what false rumor, what diabolical thing Salvato was reported to have said, I don't know nor do I know why or how it was that he slipped away when he should have been in bed and walked the three miles to Salvatore Salvato's store in the dark of the night. Nor has it ever been told what was said between him and Salvato. There was no one in the store except Sam Pork, an old, frayed ne'er-do-well incapable of interfering or assisting.

When our fine old Scotch doctor, Donald McTavish, arrived he found the boy huddled up on the floor of the cold, darkened store, battered beyond all recognition. That the boy in his weakened condition ever recovered was a tribute to his tenacity of life and the skill of a good country doctor. And so a bragging, swaggering Italian ruffian continued his ugly way among us.

Winter finally gave way to Spring and Spring to early Summer.

As I was breakfasting one Sunday morning my man said, "Excuse me, Sir, but there was what one might say a slight disturbance down at the store last night." "What sort of a disturbance?" I asked. "Well, Sir, Salvato got into an argument, quite an argument if I might say so, Sir, with one of Colonel Weatherford's gardeners, and the gardener challenged him to a bout. I hear they have put up two hundred dollars a side and are to have a go at it for ten rounds Tuesday evening, but it's not known where it's to be held, on account of them not wanting a crowd. I might say, Sir, that it seems like a very dangerous thing for a gardener to do. A man might get himself killed. Salvato was in a terrible rage, and says he won't let up on the gardener 'til he has finished him for good."

I knew that if there was any one thing calculated to spoil

a pleasant Sunday morning for my old neighbor, John Weatherford, it would be just this sort of an affair, so decided to stroll across the meadow and see him. When I arrived the Colonel was at the telephone talking to Judge Bainbridge, and seeing me in the doorway, beckoned to me to come in. "Now, Judge," the Colonel was saying, "if this jackass of a Scotchman should get killed or maimed could I be held in any way responsible? Discharge him you say? God bless me I did that at seven fifteen this morning — Sunday morning at that. One thing more. If he should inflict some injury on Salvato I take it I would be quite absolved. Not likely to happen, you say? Well, perhaps not. Why don't I stop it? I would be glad to, but after discharging a man I can hardly control him. Certainly not a Scotchman with two hundred dollars at stake. No, I won't pay his forfeit — no, that's one thing I won't do. That's asking too much. All right, Judge. Thank you very much. Good-bye."

The Colonel lit his pipe and asked me if I had heard about the affair. Then the telephone rang. The butler reported that Tim Healey, our venerable village constable, was on the wire. "You talk to him, Pendleton — see what he wants. Tell him I have discharged the gardener — tell him anything." I took the telephone, explaining that I was speaking for the Colonel. "Is it yourself, Mr. Pendleton," inquired Tim. "Well, God knows it's the feet of me is wore off entirely answering the telephone, what with all the church people in the village complaining on this bit of a foight the lads up your way are talkin' on. The heart's not in me to spoil any bit o' sport the Colonel and you and Mr. Ashley and Mr. Dick Estey would be minded to arrange, but God knows the sheriff will have the hide of me if come I don't stop the lads, and would you be remindin' the Colonel that election day don't be any distance away at all at all, and me with three and a half couples o' brats and none o' 'em out to walk yet." I here interrupted, explaining that the Colonel had discharged his gardener, who was only a temporary man, and had no interest in the affair.

In that mysteriously sure and rapid way in which news travels in rural districts the entire countryside soon learned that the affair between Salvato and Thamis McWuthey, the Scotch gardener, was to be settled in a swale of land some two miles north of Marysville at seven o'clock Tuesday evening. When the day arrived nothing could persuade Colonel Weatherford to witness the bout, so George Ashley, Henry Newcomb, Dick Estey and I dined together and betook our way northward. A hotter or more sultry evening never settled down upon Dutchess County. We found a very formidable group of Millbeck citizens, representative of all sections of the town standing on a gently rising patch of meadow land and looking down into a roped arena.

Henry Newcomb sounded a true note when, in expressing the wish that he had stayed at home, he remarked that the affair was distinctly morbid rather than sporting. It was hard to believe, he said, that people could relish seeing a big, bragging prize-fighter administer punishment to a well-meaning if misguided gardener, for they had nothing against the Scotchman, and it was, as Henry said, difficult to see what they could have in favor of the Italian. Newcomb insisted that we were no better than the aristocracy of slumdom who were wont to assemble on Tyburn Hill to witness a hanging, — for such people did not come to see a contest but, rather, an ugly event.

While Newcomb had been talking, Mr. Maloney, our

leading merchant, struck three sharp notes on the bottom of an inverted tin wash tub, to the accompaniment of which Salvato strutted down to the ring preceded by a hard-bitten trainer and followed by numerous gentlemen from the metropolis bearing paraphernalia of battle. Salvato was garbed in a sky blue silk robe and took his way slowly and pompously, bowing right and left, and calling out and waving salutations to friends and acquaintances.

Colonel Weatherford's groom, Eddie Walsh, was standing a few feet from us, sandwiched in between Pat Dwyer and Will Madden, the Huntsman. Walsh is our principal exponent of the fistic art in the settlement of all disputes, and we heard him say, "It's myself wouldn't want to be in that gardener's shoes. There's murder comin' in a minute I'm tellin' you." A moment later a somber, plaintive-looking man with sandy hair and dressed in blue overalls and blue shirt appeared at the ringside. He seemed somewhat confused, then stepped quietly between the ropes. I took him to be a shy, yet dogged, determined character.

Salvato divested himself of his silk robe and appeared in a pair of flaming red fighting trunks. McWuthey, the Scotchman, slouched out of his corner still wearing his overalls. Some discussion was apparently directed against the Scotchman wearing his shirt. He reluctantly removed the garment, the gloves were put on, the tin tub sounded, and the fight started.

According to all reports Salvato had committed himself to his henchmen and followers to do certain very specific things, and some considerable money had been wagered on the prospects of his succeeding. He had undertaken to dispose of the gardener in three rounds, and as his ire against the Scotchman grew he enlarged his promises to the point of guaranteeing a complete and clean-cut knockout; certain of our uninitiated neighbors took literally the Italian's threat to put his opponent away for all time, and were tense with excitement.

To give Salvato his due he went to work with a will. He drove fast, hard and viciously at the Scotchman. He was a powerful man and possessed of a certain technique that confused an opponent during the early stages of a fight. Had he succeeded in making effective any one of a dozen blows he let fly he would have immediately ended the contest, but the Scotchman even though he apparently could do nothing effective with his hands was a master at dodging trouble. His foot work was effective and two or three times when it seemed inevitable that Salvato must land on him he ducked with surprising ability. George Ashley sized the situation up when he said, "If that Scotchman could use his hands as well as he can his feet and would once stand up to that wop we might see something; but he might as well have his hands tied." Ashley paused a moment, then continued, "It's only a matter of time when something beastly is going to happen. I've a mind to go home. What do you think, Pendleton? Let's go after the next round."

The gong sounded for the close of the second round. In just a moment the third would commence. That was to be the end. The country people steadied themselves. The atmosphere was tense with buzzing and murmuring as the combatants went to their corners. The humidity was almost beyond endurance. In Salvato's corner experts were supplying towels — fans — sponges — liniments, and all the comforts that years of experience could suggest. In the opposite corner a dour, lone Scotchman, plainly affected by the heat, mopped his face with a towel which had been neatly folded under his chair. Of a sudden we saw him rise to his feet, walk to the ropes, and look out over the crowd. It was clear he wanted to say something. One of Salvato's visiting compatriots, concluding that the Scotchman wanted to withdraw, started hooting and hissing — others took it up. The Scotchman raised his hand. Someone yelled, "Give him a chance. Let him talk." As soon as the tumult had quieted down, a deep-pitched Scotch voice with so great a burr that we could scarcely understand it, rang out; "I wouldna wish to disappoint you by ending this wee battle the noo but I hae never fecht in sae braw a heat, so I wull dispose of this purrson the neist rrund and gang awa hame."

The instant the purport of these words penetrated Salvato's consciousness he sprang from his corner infuriated and tore at McWuthey, took him unawares, and might easily have dispatched him then and there. The referee endeavored to interfere, the tin wash tub resounded again and again, but to no good effect. The crowd started shouting, "Let 'em be. Let 'em go. Let 'em fight."

Never that I can remember have I seen a man so viciously pressed and attacked as was that seemingly ineffective Scotchman by the infuriated Italian. Even Dick Estey didn't relish the spectacle. He grabbed my arm. "Good God, Arthur, the wop will kill him. Come on, let us stop the thing. There are enough of us." But before he had finished talking that brave Scotch burr sang out from the ring, "I hae a mind to commence the noo. The furrst one will be forr the wee Johnie McGregor." At that moment Salvato let drive with his right. McWuthey ducked, countered to the Italian's jaw, and we saw and heard a blow like unto nothing we had seen or heard that night. Salvato's head snapped up, and his hands dropped momentarily to his sides. He recovered, guarded himself, and stepped back, a mixture of rage and surprise, and assumed the defensive. The Scotchman followed him across the ring, saying, "I hope the wee Johnie was aboot. I'll gie you a tap noo for Carter Wheatly, the laddie that minds the hounds at the kennels. Mon, mon, but this one wull do you nae good." With that he made a quick feint with his left, followed by a blow with his right on Salvato's chin that knocked him into the ropes and left him dizzy and confused. By this time the entire assembly was roaring. The Italians in Salvato's corner were in a turmoil, gesticulating, waving towels and jabbering in their mother tongue. McWuthey never moved, never made an effort to follow up his advantage. He just stood in the center of the ring and asked Salvato if he enjoyed Carter Wheatly's wee contribution.

Goaded by this question and the cheers and calls directed at him Salvato pulled himself together, put his hands up and stepped forward. They sparred a moment, then McWuthey said, "Whist, mon, here comes one from the Kerrnel Wutherrfurd himself." Exasperated, Salvato made a vicious attempt to land a telling blow. He managed to connect, but the sting was gone, and before he could guard himself the Scotchman tore in with a blow over the Italian's eye that closed it for that evening and other evenings to come. The ringside was in a turmoil. The round was nearly over. There could not have been above a minute left to fight.

Suddenly a whistle screeched across the meadow, and with it the well known put-putting of State police motorcycles. The Italian quickly dropped his hands, beckoned to the referee, called to his handlers, and started to divest himself of his gloves, when McWuthey jumped in front of him. "Hoot mon — hoot mon, put up your hands. Put 'em up, I say. I promised to put you awa and I couldn't do different for the bonnie wee lassie doon the village, for this is my bit o' wedding present for the lassie." With an oath that elevated that form of address to realms I had never heard approached, and without so much as giving warning or taking a fighting stance, Salvato let drive at the Scotchman's face. McWuthey dodged the blow by a hair's breadth.

Then we saw a pugilistic performance that will never be forgotten by those who witnessed it. The Scotchman, disregarding any possible offensive which Salvato might have left, drew his right arm back with lightning rapidity to its full length and drove it forward with all the weight of his back and shoulders behind it. There was a heavy, dull, ominous thud and the proprietor of the Marysville general store reeled across the entire width of the ring, fell, rolled under the ropes, and lay huddled up on the grass, a limp, sodden, senseless mass. It took us some time to placate Constable Tim Healey and the State police; we could only do it by gaining the assurance of Doctor McTavish, "that although the mon would be such a sicht his faither wouldna ken him he would be right enough the morrow." And so while Salvato continued his slumbers we came away, looking, if not feeling, like any other group of semi-respectable country citizens; we agreed to meet at Colonel Weatherford's to tell him of the affair.

On the following Sunday morning I gathered up the newspapers, and, as I often did, strolled across the meadow to have an extra cup of coffee with the Colonel, and so read our papers together. As I was fixing my coffee the Colonel said, "I hear Malloney has bought the store." "Yes," I answered,

"he is going to run it as a branch of his place in the village."
"Well, that's first rate,'" said the Colonel. "He is a good man."

I took my coffee over to a comfortable lounge chair, opened the paper, and was glancing through the rotogravure section when a picture caught my eye. I glanced at it, turned the page, and was about to discard that section when something or other caused me to turn back to a picture on it, and I read, "The Glasgow Boiler Maker, Scottish pugilist, who recently arrived in this country. The 'Boiler Maker' has been in seclusion but it is now understood he is seeking a bout or two. He is credited by foreign fight fans with having the most telling wallop developed in Europe during the last quarter of a century."

The Colonel was sitting perusing the literary supplement of his favorite paper, a paragon of innocence and dignity. I contemplated him for some time, then cut out the picture, walked over and held it out to him. He looked at it, read the caption, folded the picture, tore it into small pieces, put the pieces in his pocket, looked at me over his glasses, and went back to his reading.

CHAPTER III.

Colonel Weatherford in Spain

I BUMPED into Jimmie Wentworth after the last race at Saratoga. I had not seen him since the day we donned our caps and gowns at New Haven fifteen years before. We took our mutual recognition as complimentary to our respective states of preservation and adjourned to Jimmie's room to perform the ceremony appropriate to such a meeting. It ended by Jimmie packing his bag, climbing into my car, and coming home with me to Millbeck for a day's cubbing on the morrow.

Nature may have designed a finer terrain for cub-hunting than our Garret's Gate country, but I have never seen one — a cleared plateau of vast acreage surrounded by well-wooded coverts bountifully supplied with rides.

I have hunted the region for many seasons and know that if you will only sit quietly on your horse and not rampage about, you will view the fox time after time as he crosses and re-crosses the open land, and see hound-work to your heart's content.

It is not once in a half score of seasons that a fox will leave the surrounding woods and make his point into the open country of the valleys. Why he should have selected this particular morning to go adventuring was his own concern.

Jimmie and I were standing on a rising bit of ground from which we had twice viewed the fox crossing the plateau, when we heard hounds again coming towards us and saw the fox slip by and disappear into the woods. Just as hounds passed, Will Madden, the Huntsman, came along and rode up to me, saying, "Mr. Pendleton, Sir, he be a old one. I think he be a goin' off the mountain. Come along, Sir. Come along."

Now if there is one thing in the realm of fox hunting I am opposed to it is tin-canning off the mountain at Garret's Gate on an August morning. You no sooner find yourself a mile and a half down in the bottom land than you discover that the fox has turned and up you come up again, pulling the heart out of your horse. It was probably a combination of having Jimmie Wentworth with me and my well-earned confidence in Will Madden that decided the issue.

"Come on, Jimmie," I called, "and take care of yourself, for you're headed for the roughest bit of riding in Dutchess County."

Down we went in the wake of Will Madden and what a rider he is to follow in a rocky wood ride with hounds boiling on in front! When we reached the ford on Dark Hollow Road, hounds had crossed over. Madden had been right. The fox had straightened out and set his head for the open country and we were in for it.

Madden charged through Dark Hollow Stream — then wove his way through a dense patch of firs a mile in extent, and we were at last out in the open with hounds well on in front and fairly flying towards our good Saturday country of Willowsville. Foxes are no respecters of hounds, horses or men, even under an August sun.

I had thought we were the only ones who came off the

mountain with hounds, but we were no sooner out in the open than I heard a horse galloping behind me and glancing back saw Colonel Weatherford riding hard to overhaul us.

As we were racing down to the branch at Edgeworth the Colonel, disregarding the season of the year, the temperature, or the fact that we were supposed to be only cub-hunting, went by us.

"Good Lord, is that — is that — is his name Weatherford? John Weatherford?" Jimmie asked. I nodded.

The fox headed for Round Top, sailed over the highest point, laid a course for St. Andrew's Parish, skirted it to the east, touched the fringe of Westover Woods, sank Three Spires Uplands at an unholy pace, turned sharp left-handed, ran a brilliant two mile course as straight as a bird could fly, and denned in the center of Henry Fletcher's farm, with hounds running into him from view for the last thirty rods.

As soon as we had regained our breath Jimmie rode over to the Colonel, recalled himself to his memory, and shook hands. The Colonel was evidently delighted at the reunion for I saw him slapping his thigh, and as they parted I heard him urging Jimmie to come over to luncheon.

The Colonel rode off on his steaming horse to make peace with Henry Fletcher for hunting his lands prior to the opening Meet, an unwritten law which we try to live up to. Jimmie and I rode slowly homeward.

At about nine o'clock of that fair August morning Jimmie and I were sitting on the edge of my pool in our bathing suits, feeling like lords of all creation. I was just starting to do execution on one of the famous Bender melons which Jimmie and I had picked up in Albany after the races, when he said, "Do you know old Weatherford fairly well?" "Yes,"

I said. "He is a neighbor of mine. We are old friends. I have hunted with him for years." "Well," said Jimmie, "I haven't seen him since the summer I graduated from New Haven, in fact, I've only seen him on one occasion in my life. It was in Spain. A queer little incident. He is a remarkable character. Gets what he goes after. I'd hate to combat the old man."

There was no need of my saying anything, for I knew Jimmie would have to tell me the incident; and a story with a setting in Spain about my old friend and neighbor was one I certainly wanted to hear. I waited patiently while Jimmie poured himself another cup of coffee. Finally he continued.

"You may remember that during senior year I had leanings toward architecture, and had been working to that end. Well, I decided to knock about that summer in an effort to crystallize the thing in my mind, for I was quite on the fence about it.

"One day in early September I was up in a small hill town in Spain called San Pientra where I had gone to have a look at the Church of St. Philip of Padua. Pendleton, it's one of the most exquisite things man has yet created. Why it's not better known I can't imagine, except that it's an atrocious journey to San Pientra and the accommodations are vile when one gets there.

"About three o'clock in the afternoon I made my way to the church, which I happily found deserted, and so commenced a quiet, leisurely study. It was literally a treasure house.

"After perhaps half an hour I was vaguely conscious that someone else had entered the building and was strolling about. When I had completed my inspection and taken a second look at two or three particularly beautiful bits of glass, I sat down on a rush-bottom chair toward the front of the church to enjoy a group of magnificent windows which extended from the reredos to the peak of the chancel roof. I then noticed for the first time that a priest was sitting writing in one of the choir stalls. Back of me I could hear the other visitor making his deliberate way from object to object. I had just taken a note-book from my pocket preparatory to making a sketch when I heard the door of the church open and steps coming down the center aisle. I turned and saw a young woman with a child in her arms.

"She was very young, and her large, haunting black eyes told a story of tragedy and poverty. I don't think I am given to abnormal feelings of gallantry or knight errantry, but instantly something protective surged up within me.

"The woman went to the front of the chancel and stood waiting patiently until the priest should notice her. In the meantime the other occupant of the church had come forward and was standing a few feet from me. He was a man of well over six feet, and broad of shoulder. A loose-fitting English homespun suit and formidable walking stick suggested a British army officer. He looked a masterful, impressive character as he stood there watching the little scene that was being enacted. I remember that he had his hands behind him and was gently swinging his cane back and forth like the pendulum of a clock. He would now and again stroke his mustache, worn in the manner of Lawrence D'Orsay, and even then beginning to turn grey.

"After a few minutes the priest looked up, contemplated the woman for some time, and, realizing that she was waiting to speak with him, came forward. What was said we could not hear, but it required no words to tell us that the woman was pleading as only a distraught mother can plead, and it was evident that the priest had emphatically refused her request and had not the slightest idea of altering his mind. It was also plain that he wished to be done with the business, for he dismissed her and started back to his writing.

"As the woman turned she looked full at us with an expression hard to forget, and then walked slowly past us towards the door of the church. As she came opposite to me I looked at the child. I knew nothing about such matters then, nor do I now, but I instinctively knew that all was not well.

"We heard her open the church door, pass out and gently close the door after her. Then my companion turned to me, and let me tell you, Pendleton, there was a hard, cold, set look in the man's face. His jaw was struck forward and his big shoulders were squared away. 'Would you be willing,' he said, 'to detain that woman a moment outside the church until I join you? If you can't manage that, perhaps you would follow her and find out where she lives, and look me up at the hotel. My name is John Weatherford. You'd better hurry.'

"I did hurry. I found her sitting on the church steps. I wanted to speak with her and offer some word of cheer but my Spanish was limited, and so I went down into the square.

"Presently the baby commenced crying and the woman arose and was starting slowly down the steps when John Weatherford came out. I heard him say in excellent Spanish, 'Senorita, the Padre has promised to do what you wish for your baby. Come with me.' She put a tightly closed hand up to her forehead and started to sway, but Weatherford put his arm under hers, beckoned to me, and the three of us reentered the church.

"That afternoon a deserted little girl from a far distant village in the hills found comfort and lasting contentment, for John Weatherford acted as this and that for a baby whom the doctor said would not live out the night and didn't. When he made answer to certain questions asked him by a small, frail, little priest there wasn't a saint,— no, not even the smallest cherubim emblazoned on the glass window up under the ceiling that didn't hear just exactly what the big man was saying, for he was standing, thinking and talking four square. In spite of the fact that he wasn't telling the truth, the whole truth and nothing but the truth, all you had to do was to glance up at the exquisite figure of the Virgin above the baptismal font to see that she was smiling, and if you had been close by another Figure that I was looking at, you might have heard it say, 'Inasmuch as you have done it unto one of the least of these you have done it unto me.' And our little priest made high amend, for he took his crucifix from his neck and placed it around the neck of her who sorrowed and was heavily laden.

"Senor Piesto, the village undertaker, was heard to remark the next day at Cabana's cafe that no such expensive coffin had been bought in San Pientra since the old Mayor died.

"There is still a good deal of mystery in people's minds as to how the girl from the hills ever managed to have her baby buried in one of the very best plots of the Cemetery of St. Philip of Padua, and they still remember how a tall man in a silk hat rode in the carriage with the girl to the cemetery and how his valet, Albert, followed in another carriage with flowers that are very hard to procure in San Pientra.

"I myself rode alone in the third carriage although there was lots of room in either of the others, but Weatherford would not hear of it. He said a procession would please her. And he had a carriage for the Doctor and one for Sabine Vinceni, the hotel proprietor. The last carriage was for a little man who had contracted to carve a very complete stone.

"I said these things were hard for the simple people of San Pientra to comprehend, but what they did comprehend was that on the following Monday morning a very great deal of scaffolding was put up around the venerable walls of St. Philip's Church, and some much needed repairs were begun forthwith."

Jimmie and I sat silent for a moment or two, then Jimmie said, "You tell me you know the old man pretty well?"

"Yes, Jimmie," I said, "pretty well."

CHAPTER IV.

Sound Mules

SOMEONE sitting with the Prosecutor at the next table said, "You can't get a conviction for murder on circumstantial evidence unless you prove a motive for the murder. No, you will have to show a motive." The Prosecutor turned on the speaker in evident impatience; the group of men became silent and expectant. "Motive; why I have the rope around the old scoundrel's neck right now. Don't you worry about motive. When court re-convenes I'm going to call Joe Townsly, who runs the store on the mountain; he will testify that two weeks before the murder he had cut the old man's credit off, so that he and his wife hadn't so much as a crust in the house. I'm going to show by Doc Edwards that when he brought his wife down to see him and the Doc told him she should have an operation, the man said he didn't have five cents to his name. Then I've got two neighbors who can swear that the old scoundrel lost every crop he planted this season. Motive! What better motive do you want than an empty belly and a sick wife to make a man pick up a heavy wrench, steal over to his neighbor's cabin in the night, murder him, and walk off with his savings. He admits he owns the wrench and the cotton glove that lay beside it. All the old liar will say in defence is that he hadn't been up to the murdered man's cabin in three months, and don't know how his wrench got there. I'll soon explain it to him."

Colonel Weatherford and I had stopped for luncheon en route to South Carolina quail shooting. When the prosecutor and his compatriots had departed the Colonel sat looking out of the dining-room window. I felt that we should be pushing on, but he sat smoking his pipe with no apparent thought of the hundred and fifty miles ahead of us. I was distracted from my own thoughts by hearing him mutter to himself, "An eye for an eye, a tooth for a tooth, a life for a life." He turned to me with a look of mixed perplexity and irritation on his face. "Pendleton, in the sight of the law, a man is presumed to be innocent until proved guilty, but that Prosecutor is bent on railroading that old man to the gallows, right or wrong; an old man who is destitute and with a sick wife, and by God, Pendleton, hungry and his wife hungry."

The Colonel jerked his chair closer to me. "Bless my soul, but I took a dislike to that Prosecutor. Commonwealth's Attorney! Commonwealth's Attorney! That's a fine title to give a brazen, cut-throat brigand like that. I'm going to listen to that trial if it takes all night."

The old Colonel banged on the table, summoned a waiter, paid the luncheon check, stalked out of the dining room, crossed the street and elbowed his way into the small, crowded court-house, looking for all the world like a Lord Chief Justice in shooting tweeds.

Finding no seats available he beckoned impetuously to the surprised marshal of the court and requisitioned two chairs to be placed where he could see and hear the proceedings. The jury filed in, the judge was ushered to the bench, the prisoner led to his place, counsel arranged themselves at their table, and the local reporter whittled a new point on his stubby pencil. The trial had been resumed.

I surveyed the *dramatis personae:* the tall, kindly-looking judge with studious face; the small, frail, aged prisoner with the wisp of grey beard which he nervously stroked; the prosecutor, a blatant, cynical, hard featured man with an obviously expansive ego and finally the prisoner's attorney, whose huge bulk and rugged but dissipated face arrested me. "Who is he?" I whispered to my neighbor. "Thadeus Tremone," he answered. "He has not been in court for five years. He's drunk most of the time. He was the greatest lawyer in these parts afore liquor got him; could have been judge of the high court. It's a shame, ain't it? Folks don't know why he ever took this case. That old mountaineer ain't got a chance. He'll hang. He don't look bad, but sometimes they'd fool you. He's good as hung now."

For one long, noisy, turbulent hour the courtroom echoed with the Prosecutor's threats, implications and accusations. The abject poverty and dire distress of the bewildered little man in the pen and of his wife were heralded abroad in raucous, belligerent tones so that all might hear. "He is a rapacious, covetous scoundrel," roared the Prosecutor. "Having made a failure of his own farm and of his own affairs he looked with covetous eyes upon his neighbor's better fortune. He wanted money; money at any cost. The result was murder." As a final gesture he paraded his huge fist before the old prisoner's face promising that he, the Prosecutor, with the help of the twelve very intelligent men constituting the jury, would put the prisoner where he would not again be tempted; and thus he closed the Commonwealth's case. The State had done its best.

[47]

During this long, vicious tirade Thadeus Tremone sat slumped in his chair somnolent and indifferent. An air of tense expectancy now spread through the room. A great hulk of a man with bloodshot eyes, flushed face and trembling hands, his garments creased and disorderly, rose slowly and unsteadily to his feet, towering above those around him. "Will the Clerk do me the kindness of ascertaining whether — whether," he hesitated, then started fumbling vaguely through the pockets of his coat and finally extracted a crumpled scrap of paper, read it with seeming difficulty, then continued, "Will the Clerk ascertain whether my two witnesses, Dr. Robert Huntley, the veterinary surgeon, from Mountboro, up in London County, Virginia, and Mr. Gately, of the Railroad Company, are in the courtroom?" The man's voice slipped into one's ears as gently as a soft spring mist might drift in through an open window to fill the niches of a room.

Upon ascertaining that his witnesses were present, Thadeus Tremone stepped slowly towards the judge's bench. "Your honor, my learned opponent, the prosecuting attorney has laid great stress, Suh, in his able presentation of this case, upon the fact that my client was in extreme need of money, and that this need caused him to commit murder. Your honor, my client is in need of money, abject need. He is sixty-nine years of age, and he has been in this same need his life long. My opponent has also contended that my client is by nature rapacious, covetous, grasping and designing. Your Honor, I ask the permission of this court to address the jury in the rôle of a teller of a story, and I undertake, Suh, to connect properly my story with the testimony of my witnesses who will give evidence later as to my client's character."

The lawyer stepped in front of the jury box and quietly surveyed the twelve men who were to pass judgment upon his client. "Gentlemen of the jury, I will ask you to travel back in your memories to the days of the Great War and to the mountainous regions of our State."

Thadeus Tremone paused, crossed his arms, rested them on the rail in front of the jury box, then continued in that deep, telling, appealing voice that must have penetrated into countless jurymen's hearts.

"Gentlemen, one night when that Great War was raging on all the fronts of Europe, the mountaineers of our Carolina heard an unfamiliar freight pounding down through the mountains at an unusual hour. Trainmen said, 'Just another special freight through to seaboard without advance notices. No use advertising things in war times,' and sent word down the line to the next station,— and no further.

"In an old, rattling, flat-wheeled caboose car pounding along at the end of the train sat two men — the one representing the railroad, the other a veterinary surgeon. In front of them in box cars rode seven hundred and twenty mules, twenty-four to the car, worth $200,000 at seaboard. Across the sea the forces of war were pressing on; at seaboard a ship was waiting for her cargo.

"The train had crossed the height of land, and was starting down the long descent to sea level. A dozen times the railroad man had left his seat and paced uneasily up and down the narrow aisle. It was no secret to him that those freight cars were dilapidated, — worn out.

"The roar and rattle of the flat wheels and rickety cars grew louder and louder as the train clattered down the mountains with ever increasing speed. To the railroad man it was more than human nerves could stand. Seven hundred and twenty mules — worse, seven hundred and twenty mules due at seaboard and needed overseas.

" 'By God, something will let go,' he shouted to the veterinary.

"The swaying train pounded on. Then there was a crash. Something had let go.

"In the faint light of early morning the veterinary surgeon peered into two upturned freight cars at the bottom of an embankment. Through a forced opening fear-crazed mules fought their way out. 'Forty-four — forty-five — forty-six,' counted the veterinary surgeon. 'Forty-six.' He peered into the cars. 'There won't be any more,' was what he said.

"At the coming of the dawn a funeral fire lit up the mountains of the Carolinas, for orders are that wrecked cars shall be burned.

"Gentlemen, they couldn't hold that train, for down at seaboard a British skipper was gazing expectantly westward to the mountains. He was destined to thread troubled waters, and he would be off.

"Attracted by the fire of the wreckage, an elderly farmer had wandered down from his meagre mountain home and stood contemplating the conflagration. He was a small, spare bit of a man with a thin gray beard.

" 'Neighbor,' said the veterinary surgeon, 'there are forty-six mules running loose on this mountain.'

" 'I seen 'em, Mister, when I come down,' replied the old mountaineer.

" 'Well,' continued the veterinary, 'if I come back here in ten days do you think you could have those mules caught and cared for if I were to pay you $20 for every sound mule?'

"There was a long silence broken only by the crackling of the sun-dried wood of the burning freight cars. Then the old man answered, '$20 for the sound mules — I reckon I could.'

"The train pulled out and continued to seaboard. Ten days later two men sought and found the farm of an old hill-man in the mountains of the Carolinas.

" 'Good day, neighbor,' said the veterinary. 'About those mules — how did you make out?'

" 'I ketched 'em. They're down in the woods yonder.'

"The veterinary surgeon counted and inspected the mules. Gentlemen of the jury, there were forty-six mules in those woods. The railroad man sat down on a nearby stump and drew a check for the recovery and keep of forty-six mules at $20 a head, or $920, and handed it to a wistful, gray-haired little man who had cast his lot on that isolated, grudging mountainside, barely existing on the scanty fruits of his hard labor."

Thadeus Tremone paused.

"Gentlemen of the jury, the mountainer took that check, looked at it, studied it in silence, folded it once, folded it again, then tore it into small pieces, and held the scraps in his thin, brown fingers. 'Mister,' he said, 'she and me had a boy. She and me ain't able to say the place they buried him over there, but she kin spell it right good. Mister, I ain't seen nobody to show the picture of him in his uniform since ever I got it. Would you like to see the picture of her'n and my boy? I would kinda like for you to see it, and Mister, all them mules ain't sound, and I don't want no unsound mules agoing over where her'n and my boy is aburied'."

At six o'clock Colonel Weatherford and I were still sitting in the court room. It was the supper hour and the court was deserted. The jury had been in their room deliberating for an hour. The judge had retired to his chambers, and counsel to the neighboring hotel. In one corner the Clerk dozed with his feet on a low rail. In front of us sat the old mountaineer with his frail, anxious little wife beside him. Now and again she would glance at the grim door behind which the jury deliberated, and then pat the old man's arm reassuringly.

Two men passed by the open window leading a hound. The one said, "It seems like it would be a good night for huntin'." The prisoner glanced out of the window.

On we sat, and when I again glanced towards the west, night was creeping over the fringes of the sky. A colored man, with a deep, mellow voice, strolled by singing softly, "The Good Lord's Awaitin'." Colonel Weatherford reached over and closed the window. We waited on.

Many years later the Colonel and I were again rolling down South to shoot. The Colonel was driving while I vaguely contemplated a road map. I felt the car slowing down and heard the Colonel say, "Pendleton, do you remember the afternoon, years ago, we spent in that court house?" The car had come to a stop. I looked up. There was the small red brick building and the hotel on the opposite corner. Some miles further on, the Colonel said, "I made that old man a loan the night he was acquitted. He repaid me at the rate of two dollars a month. It took him eight years. He never missed a payment. At Christmas time of the first year I asked him to let me cancel the balance. He reproved me."

CHAPTER V.

In Maryland

A PLEASANT afternoon in May found me sitting alone on the porch of Governor Baxter's ancestral home in Maryland and looking across countless acres of well-kept pastures.

Having spent the morning talking blood lines with my old friend and looking over his brood mares, I was idling away a lazy afternoon reading Locke's "Beloved Vagabond."

In the distance a score of yearling colts romped and heckled one another along a stream bottom, while across the stream the more demure fillies gossiped under the shade of an ancestral pasture oak. In other far reaching fields the labors of husbandry were going forward.

A rhythmic tapping recalled me from my book. Looking down at my companion, an ancient collie, I saw his tail beating a tattoo on the stone floor, and his eyes focused on the driveway.

A tall, venerable figure dressed in black was approaching the house.

The dog arose, and in that sedate way common to old house dogs who live in peaceful, dignified environments, he walked down to meet and welcome the visitor.

The old gentleman leaned down, patted the collie's head, and came his slow way up the steps. He saluted me by raising his large black hat and inquired whether the Governor was at home. Upon my telling him that he was abroad but expected within the hour the old gentleman inquired, "Have I the honor, Suh, of addressing a guest of Governor Baxter?" "Yes," I replied. "My name is Pendleton. I am staying a day or two with the Governor." He made a genial bow, welcomed me to Maryland, extracted and consulted a ponderous time-piece, then walked over and rang the front door bell.

When the servant appeared, I heard him say, "Gable, Governor Baxter would wish Mr. Pendleton and me to drink his health at this hour. You will bring us juleps, and Gable, mind you serve them in My Lady's Manor Horse Show goblets."

Turning to me he continued, "It is the custom, Suh, of some of our horse shows to award silver goblets appropriate for a julep, but I regret to say, Suh, that they are not all of a size commensurate with Maryland hospitality."

The old gentleman sat down, wiped his forehead, for the day was warm, and rested himself from the fatigue of his walk. He was a survivor of a fast disappearing type, tall, erect, and made in the mold of a legendary ancestor.

When the frosted trophies arrived he arose and in a stately manner drank my health; then we both drank to the continuing prosperity of our host's affairs, and composed ourselves to contemplation and enjoyment.

My mind was drifting off to a reflection upon the acme to which comfort and well-being had been brought in the goodly State of Maryland, when my companion said, "Mr. Pendleton, might I inquire, Suh, where you make your home?" "In Millbeck, New York," I told him.

If such a thing as sitting more erect were possible, then the old gentleman straightened himself. An anxious, expectant look crossed his face as he leaned towards me and said, "Mr. Pendleton, Suh, are you acquainted with my friend, Colonel John Weatherford, of Millbeck?" "Yes," I replied. "He is a neighbor of mine. Millbeck is but a small place. We are old friends."

With noticeable effort he arose, and coming over to where I was sitting, said, "My name is Chiddingford. Major Richard Chiddingford, Suh. It is a great pleasure, I may say, a very great pleasure, Suh, to meet a friend of Colonel Weatherford's. I make you doubly welcome to Maryland, and wish my affairs would permit of my entertaining you, Suh, in a manner a Chiddingford would wish. You would be doing me a kindness by telling me of my friend's health and the state of his affairs, for it is many years since I have seen him or even heard report of him." I gladly gave the Major a brief account of Weatherford's activities, following which he lapsed into a prolonged silence. Suddenly he looked over at me, seemed to be appraising me, then said, "If I have your permission, Suh, I would welcome the opportunity of recounting a dramatic incident in my family life in which Colonel Weatherford played a part." I assured the Major that anything relating to Weatherford would be of great interest to me and begged him to proceed; so he continued.

"I am among the last of the Maryland Chiddingfords, Suh, for our line has all but run its course. The affair has to do with my niece, Mrs. George St. Ledger, my late brother's only child. She inherited our ancestral acres, and shortly thereafter married George St. Ledger, a splendid fellow, Suh, a master horseman, but as is true of many such fine sportsmen, not gifted in matters of business.

"Upon his death my niece's property was greatly impaired. I will not trespass upon your time to narrate the deplorable details, but will pass on to a certain Friday in November.

"On the morning of that day my niece's servant rode into my place with a note asking me to come to her. I ordered my horse and went at once. Mr. Pendleton, Suh, I am not able to describe in how pitiful a state I found her affairs.

"She falteringly told me how, induced by the artifices of a young man connected with a broker's office in Washington, she had intrusted him with her few remaining securities, hoping to improve her condition through speculation under his guidance. It now appeared that through some unexpected affair connected with what she called 'Wall Street,' she had lost her securities, and for reasons quite incomprehensible to her, appeared to owe the young man's firm a very large sum of money.

"This was not all, Suh. A second mortgage in the formidable sum of $16,000 on her home had been called for immediate payment. This mortgage had been placed on the land by her late husband, and the proceeds largely invested in cattle during a very bad year.

"Unhappily the mortgage was held by a person by the name of Joseph Flintbride, a neighbor, who had come into our country a few years before, from no one knows where, and had engaged in the breeding of thoroughbred horses. I might say, Suh, that this person's methods of conducting his affairs were not a credit to himself or the State of Maryland. Both his servants and himself had been in continual altercation with officials and stewards of our race tracks. His horses had been ruled off, his jockeys set down, and his trainer's license revoked, more than once.

"Flintbride had now commenced foreclosure proceedings, and the Washington brokerage firm with which the young man was connected had placed their affairs in the hands of their solicitors. It thus appeared inevitable that we were to lose the home that had been the family heritage through many generations, and that my niece was to be reduced to actual destitution and want.

"At this time my niece's daughter was attending a fashionable school up in the State of Connecticut, which I believe to be one of your older States. The child was a great beauty, and in high favor, as all of the women of my family have been, Suh, and my niece could not bring herself to face the effect her losses were bound to have on her child's future."

The old gentleman partook of his julep, rose to his feet, took a short turn of the terrace, stood in front of me, and with deep emotion continued, "It is impossible, Suh, for me to describe my feelings as this picture was unfolded. My niece was considered one of the most gracious and charming women in the State of Maryland, and I stood there, Suh, as the head of my family, unable to render her the assistance it was my duty and would have been my pleasure to render. My own affairs, I might say, had been very involved for some years.

"Only one final chance remained. It had been my niece's pleasure," the Major continued, " to raise a thoroughbred yearling or two each year which were always shipped to the sales at Saratoga. Three years before, she had bred a particularly fine appearing chestnut colt by Superman out of Mary Lambert by Knight of the Thistle, called Superchance, which met with an accident, and so could not be shipped to the sales, and my niece had been persuaded by a local trainer, George Carteret, to let him take the colt and train it for her. The colt's bad luck continued to hamper it. It was prevented from racing as a two-year-old, and again met with an accident in the spring of its three-year-old form, and so was only able to get to the track for the fall meetings. This George Carteret was a capable trainer, honest as the day was long, and devoted to my niece, for his father had once been foreman to our family. He realized full well the need of winning a race for my niece, and if possible at long odds, and so had been secretive about the colt, a phase of racing, Suh, which is very distasteful to me.

"As I said before, it was Friday of the week. On the following day, Saturday, the colt was to make its first start in the Maryland Junior Championship Stakes at a mile and a quarter, of the value of $15,000. The reigning favorite was a bay colt by Sun's Rays out of Margery Eaton by Desmond, called Sun Up, which, through a coincidence, belonged to this same Joseph Flintbride. This was an exceedingly fast colt and thought to have the class of its field, as was indicated by the odds, which were very unattractive, whereas my niece's colt was quoted at 15 to 1. The Flintbride colt could possibly outrun the Superman colt, but Carteret was convinced that it had a very faint heart, whereas my niece's entry had real courage, the courage to keep trying to the last stride. Carteret further insisted that there was no other horse in the race which could make his charge even extend himself, and that no one but himself knew how good our colt really was. He felt that were we to press Flintbride's entry for the entire route the latter's lack of heart would show itself before the finish. Knowing that my niece's affairs were very involved and that she had desperate need of money, Carteret had counseled a very small wager at these attractive odds, but had explained the risks involved, which he knew to be very real.

"Well, Suh, my niece, in desperation, seeing no other chance of saving her property and protecting her daughter, had marshalled her remaining resources — all of her resources, Suh — even including the value of her jewelry — $4,000 it was, and had recklessly wagered it on her colt. She had broken the odds through her impetuous method of conducting the business, but nevertheless, stood to win $49,000. As the hour of the event approached, the strain had become too great and she wished to confide in me as her only relative. Mr. Pendleton, my life and training, Suh, had not fitted me to cope with a situation which appeared so disastrous, for having been born and brought up with thoroughbred horses I knew only too well by what a thin thread my niece's fortunes hung.

"We sat together in front of the open fire for an hour or more while she talked of her daughter and of the many plans she had formulated for the child, and of the old place that had been in our family for so many generations. I myself had been born in the house, and an insufferable depression settled over me. Under ordinary circumstances I might have hoped for assistance from some old friends, but things were very bad in our section at that time. My niece had no other security for a loan. For myself I had nothing.

"I finally excused myself and went out on the broad terrace thinking to walk up and down and so clear my brain. Of a sudden Colonel John Weatherford's name came into my mind. Certainly he was about the last person in the world to whom I had any right to turn, and I could never understand why his name should have come to me in my distress. The Colonel, who is one of the best informed men on thoroughbred blood lines, had honored me from time to time by conferring with me about certain breeding matters, and I prided myself that he entertained some regard for my knowledge. As you know, Suh, he was brought up in a very different school from myself and has played a part in important affairs. I looked upon him as a masterful, resourceful personality.

"Although feeling that nothing could possibly be done to relieve my niece's distress, yet I wished the solace of having this confirmed by some one more conversant with such matters than myself, for I shrank from the responsibility of doing nothing. Knowing the Colonel to be in our neighborhood on one of the visits he occasionally made to inspect his brood mares, I dispatched a colored boy to three or four places where I thought he might be, with a note telling him that I would welcome an opportunity of waiting upon him for a few minutes on a matter of importance at as early an hour as he might find convenient. Within the hour the boy returned with word that the Colonel would call upon me at my niece's at two o'clock.

"Colonel Weatherford listened to my niece's explanation of her affairs, Suh, with great interest and sympathy. He was plainly distressed, as any man of gallantry would have been, and I regretted having inflicted our affairs upon him, feeling that I had permitted myself to take advantage of hospitality. The Colonel remained silent for some time, evidently searching for some straw which might alleviate the deplorable situation, but finally turned to me, saying, 'My dear Major, it seems impossible to discover any remedy or relief for Mrs. St. Ledger's distress other than the hope that her colt will give generously of his best — his very best to-morrow, and carry her colors to victory.' The Colonel invited us to lunch with him in town on the morrow before the races and would not hear of our refusing."

Old Major Chiddingford paused and sat musing on the memories that were being awakened. "Mr. Pendleton, Suh," he continued, "the recollection of that luncheon comes back very vividly to me. As a young man I had read a book pertaining to the French Revolution. I had forgotten all of the facts concerning that dastardly affair — all but one. I could never forget the fortitude and high courage — splendid, magnificent courage, Suh, displayed by the best blood of France when their hour arrived to march to the guillotine. The gaiety at their last meagre repasts — the bold shows of farewells — the smiles — the cheery waving of hands — the light, airy steps of beautiful women and gallant men. Mr. Pendleton, Suh, those brave scenes came back to me many times during that luncheon, and I could but salute my niece, for her's was the same high courage. Never, Suh, have I been privileged to listen to such spirited conversations as she engaged in with Colonel Weatherford. The Colonel, in the bigness of his heart, carried her so completely out of herself that time after time I could but marvel to hear them making bold plans for the future. Then suddenly I would see my niece wince — wince, Suh, at the sudden realization of the thing that was hanging over her. I saw her smiling and laughing with her mouth while fear and despair were in her eyes. Then we went to the track.

"Courage. What a quality that is, Mr. Pendleton, in a woman or a race horse. Why, Suh, my niece greeted her many friends and acquaintances who wished her good luck, with the nonchalance of one having nothing more at stake than the casual winning or losing of a cheap claiming race.

[61]

"I have no recollections of the first two races. I seem not to have seen them. The third event was ours. I suppose, Suh, it was my dread of the race that caused every event to happen with such rapidity. I suddenly realized that the horses were on the way to the post. There was no form of universal cataclysm that I would not have welcomed — anything which would have delayed the start of that race, or better still, have blotted out the track and all about me. I saw the colts lined up and recognized my niece's blue-and-white colors. Every time a colt would turn from the barrier and delay the start I breathed a sigh of relief. Then the flag dropped. The air was charged. 'They're off!' 'They're off!'

"For an eighth they ran together, then from the ruck a bay horse stuck its nose in front and gradually increased its lead to two lengths. Mr. Pendleton, Suh, there are two requisites of a great horse, action and class. Class, Suh, is character, action is power. Turf history has been made by horses possessing both of these qualities. Flintbride's horse had as fine running action as I ever saw in a racehorse. It had slipped easily into the lead, but the boy on my niece's colt went after it, caught it, and the pair raced on together. George Carteret had instructed his boy to press Flintbride's colt every step of the way, and, Suh, he did so. Pressed it at every stride. It was a splendid, stirring duel, Suh. My niece's colt, through being so constantly rated along, would now and again gain a trifling advantage, but the other colt with its smooth, beautiful way of moving, would easily overtake him and again step into the lead. Against the average run of horses ours would have been accounted a top colt, but, Suh, unless Flintbride's colt tired or took to sulking it seemed unbeatable.

"At times my interest in the horses obliterated my fears of

the result, then the whole tragedy of the affair would sweep over me and I would literally look away. Think of it, Suh, a Chiddingford turning his head from a horse race; I pray, I have not discredited myself with you by this admission. The horses entered the stretch. The bay colt was leading but our Superchance was at his shoulder running strongly and pressing his opponent at every stride. A generous horse, Suh, of superb courage and giving everything he had to give. The crowds were roaring: 'Come on you, Sun Up. Come on you bay horse.' It was the favorite. It seemed, Suh, as though the whole world was trying to defeat us. Just then my own over-wrought feelings were much affected by my niece's old colored retainer who had accompanied us and was standing in a passageway holding our rugs. I heard his familiar voice pleading, 'Oh, Lawd Jesus give my Miss Nancy's colt some mo' foot. Quick Lawd! Give him some mo'.'

"There was just one thing my niece's jockey could do, drive his mount every foot to the finish. The boy went to his bat. The colts' heads were together. Then our colt stepped into the lead. Never, Suh, did I live through such a moment. The horses were not above a dozen strides from the finish. Flintbride's boy could not afford to sit still, so he made a quick flourish with his whip, his mount lengthened his stride and was again in front, but suddenly, Suh, we saw Flintbride's colt's ears go back, saw him deliberately shorten his stride and start to sulk and fold up. My niece clutched my arm. I heard Colonel Weatherford mutter, 'By God, we have him beaten.' But, Suh, it was too late, a hair's breadth too late. Flintbride's colt had won the Maryland Junior Stakes.

"They tell us, Suh, that many things cross a person's mind at the moment of drowning. Mr. Pendleton, the whole panorama of my niece's distress flashed before me in all its details. Our old manor house, the little girl away at school — the old servants on the place, the great oak trees in the pastures under which so many notable horses had been raised. Even such trifling things as the grey stone spring house. All these old associations raced through my brain.

"People started surging down towards the track, the betting ring and paddock, many of them to collect on the result of the race, while we three stood silently watching the moving throng. Presently my niece put her arm within mine, touched my hand, and said, 'Uncle Richard what do you favor for the last race?' and smiled at me, Mr. Pendleton, in a way no man of spirit could ever forget.

"I dreaded the thought of subjecting my niece to the dreariness of spending the first evening of her now changed condition alone or even with me, who had so little of cheer to offer. I accordingly importuned Colonel Weatherford to accompany us to dinner, and made bold to hint to him that it would be a great kindness to my niece. He had planned to travel to New York immediately following the races, but at once changed his plans and accepted our invitation.

"Before leaving the track my niece communicated with her servants at home, and Mr. Pendleton, Suh, no three people in the State of Maryland sat down to a finer dinner than did we on that evening. It was not only worthy of a victory, Suh, but even of a defeat. The oysters of that particular autumn were very favorably commented upon, and I had presented my niece a day or two before with a pair of canvas-back ducks of the very primest order.

"In honor of our guest my niece served her Elizabeth D. Williams Madeira. I have not been privileged, Suh, to partake of your northern hospitality and so do not know in what esteem wine from the island of Madeira is held in the North, but we of Maryland took pride in our stocks of such wine which we always referred to by the name of the ship in which the wine had completed its conditioning. My niece had inherited such Madeiras as Nancy Lippincott, Henry P. Calvert, Charles Carroll, Mary Steward, and others equally illustrious, but it was a tradition of my family that, due to the reported excellent condition of the vines of that particular year, no finer Madeira was to be found in Maryland than the Elizabeth D. Williams.

"And just before coffee was to be served my niece spoke with me aside, handed me the key to her wine cellar and it was my privilege, Suh, to bring her a bottle of 1838 Cognac, Grande Champagne Cognac, Suh, from the Charente. When this noble brandy had been served the Colonel held the old Waterford brandy goblet in his hand until the contents had taken some of the warmth of the touch, revolved the goblet, slowly enjoying the aroma, and was contemplating the goblet and its contents when we were startled by hearing him say in a very emphatic manner, 'Why God bless my soul, that's it, that's it, that's where it was. That's it.' My niece and I looked up at him in surprise, and Mr. Pendleton, I was alarmed, greatly alarmed, Suh. I could only think he had been taken by a seizure. He was sitting there with the goblet raised in the air staring straight in front of him, and remained thus for some time with the most unaccountable expression on his face. Then, apparently recalling the glass in his hand, he again revolved it in order that the brandy, as it spread over the surface might further augment the aroma; took a sip, put the glass down, turned and said to my niece, 'Mrs. St. Ledger, I

[65]

had expected to return to New York tonight on the sleeper. I have changed my plans. I will stay here two days if you can put me up.'

"Well, Suh, when these arrangements had been made the Colonel seemed to dismiss whatever had upset him. He joined me in having another drop of brandy and told us much of the country of the Champagne, in the Department of Charente, of the difference between Grande Champagne, Fins Bois, Petite Champagne, and others, and of the making of fine wines and brandies. When we adjourned to the drawing room my niece, upon Colonel Weatherford's insistence sat at the piano and sang to us, and, as though determined that the evening should be one of good cheer in so far as he could make it so, the Colonel, whom we found had a splendid voice, sang with her. They drifted from one song to another until the clock reminded us that midnight was striking.

"After the Colonel had retired and while I was assisting my niece in putting out the lights she put her hands on my shoulder, saying, 'Isn't he the grand seigneur? We never could have seen the evening through, just you and me alone, could we? Oh, Uncle Richard, where do I start in the morning? What does one do when one has nothing?' Mr. Pendleton, Suh, I was very much affected by her words and her distress.

"Being a light sleeper I awoke early the next morning and arose, thinking to stroll over to my own cottage and rout out my servant to prepare breakfast. As I started across the lawn one of my niece's colored boys drove into the place. Assuming the rascal to have been abroad all night with his employer's car I went over to take him to task. The boy explained that before it was yet light a large gentleman had awakened him, pulled him out of bed and ordered him to drive him into Baltimore. Upon questioning the boy I found that he had driven the Colonel to a public garage where the Colonel rented a car and driver, telling the proprietor that he would probably need the car for two days. The Colonel then sent a message to my niece to the effect that he would not be back until the day following.

"Well, Suh, the Colonel reappeared just before the dinner hour on Monday, looking, I thought, weary and much traveled, but gay and vigorous as always. He craved my niece's indulgence for being such an unceremonious guest, and went up to change.

"We had but half finished dinner when, in response to a ring of the door bell the servant announced Mr. Flintbride to see Mrs. St. Ledger. At the very sound of the man's name my niece's hands covered her face as though trying to shield her from a distressing vision, and she looked appealingly at me. My indignation rose, Mr. Pendleton, and I had every desire to horsewhip the rascal. I am sure, Suh, I do not have to inform you that mortgages are never called in our section of the State of Maryland. One does not contemplate such an extraordinary proceeding any more than one would expect one's personal friend or family bank to remind one of a slight indebtedness. I pride myself, Suh, that certain of my valued friends have been indebted to me for thirty years, while others have held my notes of hand for quite as long a period. I would not mention such trifles nor expect others to mention them to me. Colonel Weatherford, however, suggested the wisdom of Mrs. St. Ledger seeing the man while we were in attendance upon her. My niece consented but appeared apprehensive of incurring Flintbride's ire by keeping him waiting, and thought we should see him at once. The Colonel, however, announced in no uncertain language that there was not a man in this or any other country for whom he would leave such a rack of lamb and 1865 Chateau Lafitte, and advised letting the scoundrel cool his heels, upon which we resumed our dinner. We finally withdrew to the drawing room where Flintbride awaited us.

"A more repulsive individual than this Flintbride would be difficult to picture, Suh. He had been drinking heavily in celebration of his recent victory, and instead of having become convivial and gracious, as good wine makes those of gentle birth, he had become surly, vindictive and repulsive to contemplate. He was a tall, powerful, hawk-like man of an ungovernable temper. Vexed at our delay, he merely nodded to Colonel Weatherford and me, then strode defiantly up to my niece, and with no preliminary words, said, 'My lawyers tell me that the people representing you are trying to get an adjournment of the foreclosure proceedings — that you want more time — want to stall the thing along. Now listen to me. If you can't pay the mortgage today you won't be able to pay it tomorrow or next week or next month. There is going to be no adjournment for a day or any other time. I have made plans to put a foreman on this place on January first, and must know where I stand, and I don't mind telling you I am moving in here myself as soon as I can get the place cleaned and put to rights. These d——— lawyers have a way of granting favors to each other and letting their clients whistle, so I want you to tell your people to let the thing take its course.'

"I started to rise, Suh, to order the scoundrel from the house, when my attention was directed to Colonel Weatherford. He stood up, stamped over to the door, closed it with a bang, locked it, jerked the key out of the key hole, put the key in his pocket, walked rapidly and determinedly over to the fire-place, turned, faced Flintbride, and said, 'Flintbride my man I have some things to say to you.'

"Mr. Pendleton, Suh, this Flintbride was not the sort of person, drunk or sober, you could lock in a room. He had lived a great part of his life in environments where men act first and think afterwards, and remember, Suh, he was in his cups. I could not see his full face at the moment, but it was evident he had become inarticulate with passion. His neck and such of his face as I could see had turned a deep scarlet. Then his voice came to him. 'Open that door. Open that door, I say, or by God I'll,' and with that, Suh, he whipped a revolver from his pocket. I jumped to my feet, but the Colonel indicated in a very decisive way that he would not brook interference on my part. Flintbride was standing facing the Colonel and holding the pistol in his hand. His voice had changed to a low, hard snarl. 'For the last time, unlock that door,' he said. The words were no sooner out of the man's mouth than Colonel Weatherford turned on him with a fierceness that fairly astounded Flintbride as it did all of us. 'Flintbride,' he said, 'I'll unlock that door when I have finished with you, at which time, with Mrs. St. Ledger's permission, I will have one of her servants throw you out of the house.'

"Upon saying this the Colonel, entirely disregarding Flintbride, crossed the room, picked up a package which was lying on the table, returned to his place and slowly and deliberately removed the wrappings. My apprehension was such that I was keeping my eyes riveted upon Flintbride. Suddenly I saw him step rapidly backwards. I looked over at the Colonel and saw him holding a small black book in his hand and looking Flintbride full in the face. I arose and crossed the room. Mr. Pendleton, Suh, I never looked upon a face so dominated by passion as was Joseph Flintbride's at that moment, but he stood there without uttering a word. The room was oppressively silent. My niece was sitting on the edge of her chair, bewildered and alarmed. Suddenly Colonel Weatherford stepped forward until he was not above a yard from Flintbride; then he shot out his right hand and pointing his forefinger straight at the man's face, said, 'Flintbride, you ran a four-year-old colt in the Maryland Junior Stakes last Saturday, a race restricted to three-year-olds. That colt of yours was foaled some time in the month of November. You gave the Jockey Club the eleventh day of the following February as the date of foaling. The sire of that colt was standing at your place when the mare was bred and when she foaled. You had this book, which records the mares which were bred to the horse, and dates of service, in your possession.'

"The Colonel reached in his pocket, extracted a small magnifying glass, and held the glass and book out to Flintbride, saying, 'You can still see traces of the original November entry in your hand writing.' Instead of accepting the book Flintbride stepped back a few paces, looked down at the pistol which he still held in his right hand, and said, 'What business is this of yours? Who the hell are you?' The Colonel stood contemplating him for some time, then continued. 'Flintbride, let me tell you of certain lines along which my mind is running right now. You came into this country a few years ago and bought a very bad farm — a cold, uncharitable bit of land unsuitable for raising thoroughbred horses. You are no farmer. Gunmen never are. You happened to locate quite close to the finest bit of land in this section where horses have done well for a hundred and fifty years. You want Mrs. St. Ledger's farm. You have always wanted it. You made a loan on it prompted entirely by the belief that by so doing you would be able eventually to acquire the property. But you wanted to make doubly sure. There must be no chance of Mrs. St. Ledger having the wherewithal to discharge the mortgage. And so one day at the Pimlico race track you presented a young man to Mrs. St. Ledger — a young man associated with a so-called brokerage house in Washington. Flintbride, the law provides ways and means of ascertaining who the active and silent partners of such a firm are, and I now know the names and records of every individual constituting that firm.'

" 'Just before you called the mortgage this plausible young man gained possession of Mrs. St. Ledger's securities. Flintbride, before I have finished I propose having each and every transaction in Mrs. St. Ledger's account traced to its ultimate end. I shall not rest content until the District Attorney, Prosecuting Attorney, or Department of Justice, or whoever handles such matters, goes to the bottom of this thing.

" 'Now, then, my man,' continued the Colonel, 'I am going to give you just three minutes to decide whether or not you stand ready to make the following restitution to Mrs. St. Ledger. First, I want the value of the Maryland Junior Stakes turned over to her. Second, I want one-half of what Mrs. St. Ledger stood to win, paid to her. I arrive at one-half by conceding that the odds on her horse would not have been as favorable had your colt not been running. And finally, I want Mrs. St. Ledger's securities or their present values returned to her. We shall also require a general release from all claims by your firm. Mrs. St. Ledger on her part will pay off the mortgage which you now hold on her property with all interest to date and the statutory charges incurred in connection with the foreclosure action.

" 'Further than this I will require you to retire your colt and neither race it again as a three-year-old nor permit others so to do.

" 'I wish to make it quite clear, Flintbride, that my conjectures respecting the treatment accorded Mrs. St. Ledger by your firm are only conjectures. I may be doing both the firm and yourself an injustice. If I am, you are at liberty to refuse to return the securities or their value, but in this event I shall apply myself energetically to going to the bottom of the matter. As I said, I will give you three minutes to make up your mind, after which I will act as I think best in the premises.' "

Old Major Chiddingford leaned over and tapped me on the knee. "Mr. Pendleton, Flintbride didn't take three minutes — he didn't take any time at all. He didn't give the Colonel an opportunity to change his mind.

"When these arrangements were consummated and Flintbride had departed, we three sat very quietly together. My niece had her back to us and we could see her occasionally lifting her handkerchief to her eyes. The Colonel touched me on the arm, pointed to my niece, and placed his fingers on his lips. And so we sat there without speaking. Presently he took a note-book from his pocket, wrote a few words, tore the page out and handed it to me. As a memento of that evening my niece did me the kindness of taking that little slip of paper into Baltimore and having it handsomely framed for me. It now hangs in my library:

Dear Major,

How about you and me slipping out and exploring the possibilities of a snack of cold duck and a glass of wine?

J. W.

CHAPTER VI.

"Everything Is All Right, Sonny"

THROUGH the long, quiet hours of the night the Millbeck hills and valleys lay shrouded in heavy folds of mist.

The voices of those who spend the nights afield were heard as though muffled in folds of damask; a cow calling for her calf, a solitary hound running Pecket's ridge, a house dog disturbed in mind.

In the dark of early morning a boy, mounted on a grey Royal Canopy mare poked his solitary way over the height of land which separates Little Rest Valley from Hawk's Hollow. Upon reaching the crest he halted, struck a light, and looked at his watch: five-fifteen. Hounds were meeting at Bartlett's Carry at six. He stood looking expectantly towards the east for some sign of dawn, for one could not be sure of finding one's way in the dark through the maze of sheep trails. It would, he mused, have been better to have taken the longer route by road. As he hesitated, the mare suddenly grew restless and uneasy in the spectral murkiness, and kept turning and looking intently towards the north. A dry twig snapped somewhere out in front of her in the fog and a deer passed by heading into the valley to drink. The boy spoke softly to the mare and put his hand on her neck. After again glancing skyward the boy left the height of land and threaded his way downward through great patches of sweet-fern and blueberry bushes to Hawks brook to search up and down the dripping slash for the ford at Storey's Pine.

At six-fifteen they were still aimlessly circling Thedford's Upland two miles north of Bartlett's Carry. A wan ray of light was stealing slowly across the sky, but impenetrable mist still shrouded the earth.

The boy again halted the mare and turned her towards the covert he thought hounds should now be drawing. He sat thus for some time, abstracted by his own thoughts, his head forward and his chin resting on his chest. Slipping to the ground, he drew the reins over the mare's neck, sat down on the moist, soft earth, and buried his face in his hands. The desire to locate hounds, to have them find and go away, the urge to feel the grey mare galloping under him — all these things had left him. There had been no sense, he thought, in coming cubbing, not at Bartlett's Carry of all places. It had been so much better to have ended his hunting after the run on Tuesday. It was only the old, incessant longing to hold fast to what little of his mother remained to him that had brought him out. This had been her favorite country. She loved the wild ruggedness of these uplands. It was on these very hills that she had taught him the science of the sport, and the picture of her as she rode so fearlessly from one headland to another awakened beyond all other pictures the memory of that comradeship which ended when he was but a youth. The years had rolled on but the old hurt and longing and loneliness never seemed to grow less. It was because of her that he had wanted to have his last day to hounds at Bartlett's Carry. Tomorrow he was to sail to the world's end to learn the difficulties of selling petroleum products, — his first employment.

Great banks of mist were being drawn skyward by the sun's rays so that he now recognized the field in which he was sitting. Below him was the in-and-out across Meecham's lane. It had been his first in-and-out — just two low, dilapidated panels, but formidable to a wee pony. His mother had given him a lead, calling back, "Come on, Sonny. Give him his head. Everything is all right."

He dropped his head on his arms as one old memory awakened another. There were eighty thousand people in the Yale bowl. If he missed the kick the score stood a tie. A Yale-Harvard tie game. One couldn't miss. Not with victory so close. But he had been dizzy for the last few moments of the game. Dizzy and uncertain. He was not seeing and thinking clearly. Then she had come to him; come to him just as she had once led him over the little in-and-out. "Everything is all right, Sonny." It was as though she were stretching her hand out to him there on the soggy football field. He remembered how clear and simple it had all become. He kicked — and there was a roar from Yale's side of the bowl.

And then there was the ugly moment down in Maryland when he went to ride old Colonel Weatherford's Carcasian. As they crossed the road and were racing down to that formidable third fence, a horse, running out of hand, bumped him when only a few lengths from the fence. Carcasian was off balance, heading kitty-cornered to the jump, and galloping a terrific pace. The end seemed inevitable. And there she was, — "Everything is all right, Sonny." With the sensitiveness and rapidity of a great violinist his hands conveyed that message, or hint or help — that thing which great horsemen contribute but know not how, — and his mount was over and racing on.

The world even as it presses close to us with all its innumerable ties and contacts, is no panacea for lonesomeness and
dependency. But she had stood by during youth's crises holding her hand out to him and giving him the feeling of being
ever near. "Everything is all right, Sonny."

Perhaps she would not be out there at the fringe where he
was going. And suppose he couldn't find her at his old haunts
when he came back, perhaps years hence. She might never
come to him again and she was his only tie; the only tie that
mattered.

The grey mare threw up her head and looked fixedly to
the west. A faint echo of hounds' voices came to him. He rose
to his feet, spoke to the mare, mounted and harked again.
The hilltops were now clear of mist but the valleys were as
grey mountain lakes nestling in the folds of the hills. Hounds
were coming rapidly toward him, and running a strong, pur-
poseful line. He heard their voices soften as they sank a deep
swale; then they entered a patch of oak trees just right handed
of him and carried the line with dash through the wood and
down into the valley and the mist.

He waited for some sign of the Huntsman or the field, but
there was no sound of galloping horses. They had lost hounds
somewhere out in the fog. He turned the mare's head towards
the valley and slipped in behind hounds.

There is now no one to write the history of that run. A
farmer at Castlebar busy at his milking heard hounds race
through his lower pastures. Dr. McTavish, returning from a
long vigil, heard their clamorous cry in Makepiece Woods,
miles, as the crow flies, from Castlebar. Joe Burrage, the car-
rier, saw them scaling the bleak slope of Penthold Head with
a straining, determined grey mare on their sterns. Miss Sarah

Prentice, the teacher, saw them boiling down from Thatcher's Uplands as she walked to school down Three Brothers lane. She was the last to see them, but old Doctor Sedgwick, praying at the eight o'clock service on St. Matthew's day, heard them as they raced up Nettleton Hill. He paused to listen, then closed his prayer book and continued, "Oh, Lord, give us the sense of enjoyment of all good things. Grant us courage and the self respect that comes from courage. Help us to learn from our games and pastimes to face life valiantly. And when we shall set out upon our last hunt, grant that we may ride forward with faith and high courage. Amen." Hounds' voices sank to a faint echo.

On the crest of Nettleton Hill stands the hundred-year-old ruin of a Dutch Manor house, its broad acres now a dreary, desolate waste. A great stone wall, still showing the pride of early workmen, looms gaunt and foreboding against the sky line. The boy took the mare gently by her head, for she was laboring, and together they rode on towards the wall.

The mare took off and tried and kept trying as only a sensitive, clean-bred mare can try. The boy had a feeling of sinking; sinking for a long, long time, and of strong noises, then of peace and quiet, and a well-loved voice came to him, "Come Sonny, let us ride forward. We can ride on together now. Everything is all right, Sonny."

CHAPTER VII.

The Horse in His Gracious Majesty's Colony of New Jersey

AUTHOR'S NOTE: The quotations appearing in this chapter were taken from records of The New Jersey Historical Society.

COLONEL WEATHERFORD and I accepted an invitation to week-end in the Far Hills country, have a few days with the Essex Hunt's blue-ticked, Eastern Shore hounds, and witness the New Jersey cup race.

Between the running of two minor events the Colonel and I were gazing off over the pleasant hills of Somerset County, each with its cottage or manor house, when two young ladies took their stand quite close to us and embarked upon a conversation of some novelty.

The first: "Do you ride?"

The second: "It's scrummy. I have a pony. Have you?"

The first: "I have a yummy pony. It's black, and a new bridle with two reins."

The second: "I wouldn't have liked to live here before there were any horses, nothing but motor cars, would you?"

The first: "That wouldn't be very scrummy. Do you want to see a new puppy that's in our car?"

They passed on. The Colonel perched his eye glasses on his nose, looked down at the young ladies as they toddled away, then turned to me, saying, "Well, God bless my soul, Pendleton, what a how-do-you-do that is. New Jersey without any horses. Nothing but motor cars. What a conception." We started to walk on when he pulled up short. "What do you know about the horses in colonial days?" he asked. "Nothing," I replied.

Some weeks rolled by when, towards the middle of December, we had a day which must have been on a par with one Keats spent in Devonshire, — "A splashy, rainy, misty, snowy, foggy, haily, floody, muddy and generally slipshod day."

We persevered with hounds as far as Three Brothers School House, then decided to abandon the sport for the day, I going on to the fixture at Highminster Gate to announce to the field, should there be one, that hounds would not go out.

Having broken the news to Dick Estey, Mary Sedgwick and a handful of other enthusiasts whom I found huddled under the school house shed, I let Jack Semple slip on towards home at any pace which commended itself to him, and overtook Colonel Weatherford in Meecham's lane splashing along with hounds. We arranged to lunch at his house on the pretext that he had something or other he wanted to read to me.

When I arrived the Colonel was in the dining room standing in front of a buffet, his legs far apart, his hands behind his back, rocking slowly on his heels and contemplating two bottles of wine, one a Madeira of 1832, with the legend, "bottled for Senor Hernandez Parrento." Below was a small sticker reading, "From the Estate of Henry Philbin, 22 Waters Street, 1851." The other, a bottle of Burgundy, Clos de Vougeot, 1883. "It is a filthy day, Pendleton," the Colonel remarked. "I have no heart for a bottle of claret. It's not that kind of a day. Which will it be? Madeira or Burgundy?" "Madeira," I answered. The Colonel stood contemplating the Clos de Vougeot wistfully. "All right, Pendleton, but don't forget that the imperial troops of France never passed the Clos de Vougeot without presenting arms."

There are few pleasanter recreations than toying over a bottle of ancient wine and chatting of this and that, and as we left the table I had the feeling that most of the world's ills had been attended to and corrected.

Upon reaching the library the Colonel gathered up two or three musty volumes bound in brown buckram, took them over to his desk, looked at me over the rim of his glasses as though he were addressing a schoolboy, and said, "Now, then, Pendleton, about there having been no horses in New Jersey in Colonial days. Nothing but motors. I located these three volumes of the New Jersey Historical Society records—they contain copies of all newspaper items published in colonial days concerning the Colony of New Jersey. There is absolutely no question in my mind as to there having been horses in colonial days. Listen to some of these advertisements and notices.

"Here is a fellow named Hugg who owned a horse called Yorick, probably a fair sort of a horse:"

Will stand this season at the house of the subscribed, the famous horse YORICK, who was imported last season by John Foxcroft, Esq.

He is a full bred hunter. He is 15 hands and an inch.

Made very strong and neat. His carriage and courage equal if not superior to any horse in America. The terms 20 shillings and a half dollar to the groom. Mares will be kept by the subscriber at 10 shillings six pence per week.   Joseph Hugg.

"You know, Pendleton, that style of advertisement rather appeals to me. It's chatty and enthusiastic. Look what old Hugg tells us about Yorick. He says he is famous, that he is a hunter, that he is full bred, that he is made very strong and neat, that his carriage and courage is equal if not superior to any horse in America, and certainly considering the difficulties of the times in which Mr. Hugg lived, with Hessian troops flying up and down the roads of New Jersey, twenty shillings seems fair enough for a horse that was neat and famous and with a carriage superior to any horse in America. Compare that advertisement with the restrained efforts of this sophisticated age." The Colonel asked me to hand him a copy of the *Thoroughbred Record*. "Now then, Pendleton, take William Woodward's advertisement of Gallant Fox. Listen.

Gallant Fox. $3,000 No Return.
Bay, 1927. By Sir Gallahad III, Marguerite
by Celt.
Property of Belair Stud.

"Very dignified and practical, but not as good reading as old Hugg.

"Hear what some of these other fellows say about their horses." He turned to the advertisements of stallions.

The brown horse, "Falstaff" of Perth Amboy was got by "Old Cade" and "is the stoutest of Cade's get."

[84]

"Young Spark" — to be kept at Peter Covenhaven's near Brunswick. "His dam by a *genteel* Mare." Any person inclining to send their mares will have them covered at three dollars for the season.

"The Raven," a three quarter blood horse, 14 hands 3 inches, and as handsome as any horse on the entire Continent. Stud fee a Pistole.

The great horse, "Hero," bred by John Holme, Esq., of Carlisle in Old England, got by "Young Sterling" by old "Sterling," 15 hands, and is allowed to be the most complete horse ever seen in America.

Mr. Rhea's "Imported Frederick." He is 15 hands, and perhaps the most complete horse in America. He was got by "Hobgoblin" out of Lord Godolphin's "Golden Lock" mare. His dam was the famous "Firetail" mare.

Mr. John Budd's horse "Swan." He stands at a Pistole at Salem, West New Jersey; stands 15 hands, and has been learnt to pace and goes as fast as any horse on the Continent. Trots and gallops very light, and runs fast.

"Pendleton, this Mr. Budd had a very notable horse in Swan. I would like to have seen him. It's no wonder he was proud of the horse. Look what he could do, 'He has been learned to pace and goes as fast as any horse on the continent. He trots and gallops very light, and runs fast.' It's a wonder Lord Howe or Sir Henry Clinton didn't take him back to England."

The Colonel paused to re-light his pipe, then went on. "The Rutherfords were a very useful, forward-looking family in the Colony and still have their roots deep in the soil of New Jersey. Listen to this announcement. They brought some fine blood into the County. Note the Childers blood in this horse."

For the Improvement of the Breed of Horses in this and the neighboring Governments:

Notice is hereby given: That there is kept at Trenton, by Mr. Robert Rutherford, a very fine stallion from Ireland, well known by the name of Young Tifter.

Young Tifter was bred by the Hon. Charles O'Neil, Esq., of Stains Castle, in Ireland, and begot by the famous Tifter brought from England by the Right Hon. Arthur Hilt, Esq.; who was begot by Tifter of Warwick, the best twelve stone horse in England. Tifter of Warwick was begot by the famous Toulous Barb, and bred out of Cream Cheeks, full sister to Leeds, and Grand Dam to Old Childers. The present Tifter's Dam was the famous Primrose, daughter to Dimple, and her dam daughter to Wasp, etc., etc.

Robert Rutherford.

The Colonel turned some pages to where he had the next marker, started to read to himself, and suddenly glared at the page as though doubting his own eyes. "God bless me, Pendleton. This is an informal and extraordinary point of view."

The noted horse, "Scipio," formerly kept by Mr. Gershorn, will stand at 50 shillings. As it is reported by designing persons that the above horse is not the noted

"Scipio," so those gentlemen who bred their mares shall have the season gratis.

"The 'noted Scipio' would appear to have lived under a slight cloud."

The Colonel went on to the next item, again reading to himself. After covering a line or two he removed his glasses, looked at them as though they must need polishing, wiped them with his handkerchief, started reading again, and immediately muttered, "God bless me. What a horse. Listen to this, Pendleton."

The Notable Horse Ragamuffin.
The property of the subscriber. Imported
from Pennsylvania.

Between 5 and 25 years of age this grass, in bad order. Will cover this season within two miles of the Church in Rahway, at 39 1/6 dollars the season. "Ragamuffin" is a very ugly white horse with gray legs, mane and tail, two black feet, star and snip; he is of full size, thirteen hands high, badly made for his height, and is allowed by very indifferent judges to be one of the worst moving, indelicate and ill looking horses in the Colony. His blood and pedigree are agreeable to his shape and movements. He was got by "Nunshi," a noted horse, who, a few years since, was rode by a gentleman, then an Adjutant in a regiment of Lazy Greys with universal ridicule. "Nunshi's" sire was "Old Deformity," of whom he had a very striking likeness; his grandsire by "Blunder," who, when about to start in a race, had the good fortune to fall, breaking his own neck and that of his rider. His brothers were "Old Slack," "Sloven" and "Inactivity," all famous horses; their performances exactly corresponding with their names. "Ragamuffin" though wanting the beauties of those Capital horses, is fully possessed of all their deformities. Those persons who choose to have their mares covered by "Ragamuffin" will be charged no more than 10 shillings per week for each mare's pasture, as they will feed on the town common.

The above horse being thought a dangerous animal, two grooms will constantly attend him during the season of covering to prevent him doing the least mischief. The grooms will expect a small fee.

(Signed) J. Stanbury.

When it finally dawned upon the Colonel that this advertisement, which so frankly and fearlessly depicted the qualities of Ragamuffin, had been inserted in the New Jersey journal by some local jester of the day, he took it in good part.

The telephone called the Colonel from his reading and he handed me one of the volumes to browse through pending his return. I left the marked items for the Colonel to read, and simply opened the book at random.

I was struck with John Millar's appraisal of his wife, Mary, but even more so with Mary's stamina.

NOTICE.

Whereas Mary Arnold, wife of John Millar, has eloped from his bed and board, and has taken away his goods and property, and has continued drunk for six weeks, and is likely to continue so, I am determined to pay no debts of her contracting.

John Millar,
Elizabethtown.

It was positively startling to see how these old books jumped from things tragic to mundane. Immediately following Mr. Millar's gallant characterization of Mary, appeared

Lieutenant General Sir Henry Clinton,
   Knight of the Bath,
       to
Lord George Germaine,
   One of His Majesty's Secy. of State.
My Lord — I have the honor to inform Your Lordship that pursuant to His Majesty's instructions, I evacuated Philadelphia at three o'clock in the morning.

And speaking of Sir Henry Clinton I am inclined to think he is worth knowing more about, for a page or two further on I again encountered him, in the role of a letter writer, brief and to the point.

"Sir Henry Clinton to William Livingston, Titular Governor of New Jersey" (It seems the Governor had written to Sir Henry in a complaining tone, that he had heard that Sir Henry had suggested to some enterprising young men that it would be a gracious act to their King were they to assassinate the Governor).

Sir Henry writes to the Governor:
"Had I a soul capable of harboring so infamous an idea as assassination, you at least would have nothing to fear for be assured I should not blacken my soul with so foul a crime to effect so trifling an end.
                     Clinton, K. B."

The book jumped from Sir Henry to Colonel Lowry's effort to dispose of a light fingered and liquor-stealing slave.

TO BE SOLD VERY REASONABLY.

A negro man (house servant) of about 32 or 35 years of age. A good tempered, ingenious, handy fellow. Can shave and dress a wig very well, and is sold for faults which will not be likely to affect a purchaser who need not intrust a servant with liquor or the laying out of money. Enquire of Col. Thomas Lowry, in Flemington, or the Printer of the Journal.

Then to Mr. Furman's wench for whom he wanted a good round sum.

A negro wench about 30 and her son about 7 years old. Both very healthy, and remarkably stout and strong. The wench is used to all kinds of country work both indoors and out. The price is $1200.

Moore Furman.

A fox hunter lost his hound and it interested me, historically, that in 1776 an owner would offer so liberal a reward.

STRAYED OR STOLEN.

A Fox Hound of a pretty large size. White with yellow spots on his side. His ears long and spotted with yellow and white, and a long tail. Whoever will leave word with the Printer or at Mr. Winan's Tavern, where the said hound may be had shall receive thirty dollars reward.

There was a note reminiscent of the problems and perplexities which beset the French and Belgian breeders during the Great War in the following notice.

The distinguished stallion, "Bay Richmond," who

was removed from Long Bridge upon the approach of the Hessians, is now returned.

Life in 1776 seemed much a counterpart of life today. People acquiring things and getting rid of them again. Social notes of those in high places jumbled together with the tragedies of those whom fortune neglected. I read on.

Having engaged myself to enter upon the work of making Epsom Salts at Little Egg Harbor, I offer my Sorrel Mare for sale. Gentlemen inclined to try her will make inquiries of the Printer.

Why the manufacture of Epsom Salts should have been inimical to maintaining a Sorrel Mare was not evident.

TO BE SOLD.

An excellent Chair horse. He is something in years, but the price will be in proportion. Also to be sold a likely young negro wench for no fault.

Benjamin Smith.

TO BE SOLD.

A handsome pair of Grey Geldings with or without a phaeton, and a negro wench with her child of two years old, a wagon, and two milch cows.

Enquire of Printer.

Yesterday being his Majesty's birthday an elegant entertainment was given by His Excellency, General Tryon, at which were present the Governor of New Jersey, etc., etc. A Toast was drunk to a speedy suppression of the Rebellion.

OLD MAN

TO BE SOLD BY THE SUBSCRIBER
IN MOUNT HOLLY, NEW JERSEY

A stout, healthy negro boy, about seven years old.
Has had small pox and measles and is warranted sound.

Henry Jones.

I was very much impressed with the openness and frankness with which victims of horse trades took the public into their confidence. There was undoubtedly a tinge of bad feeling between Mr. Cook and Mr. Egbert as evidenced by the following:

Whereas, I, the subscriber, did on the 27th day of last month purchase a black horse known as the Dutch Minister's Black Horse of Amwell, of a certain David Cook, of Readington, and in the evening of the said day he delivered in the dark a horse of 23 years of age to defraud me, and now refuses to give me the Dutch Minister's Black Horse of Amwell, this is to forewarn all persons not to trade with the said David Cook for the horse as I am determined to have him.

Nicholas Egbert.

May 1, 1778.

It interested me to stumble across a reference to Princeton University and note its flourishing condition in war times. Doctor Witherspoon seemed most optimistic.

I announce with satisfaction that although there were only 10 proper College Members at Nassau Hall last term, yet at least one instructor was constantly upon the ground, and that another professor has now been chosen.

John Witherspoon.

Never, I think, have I explored the pages of a book which touched upon so many authentic, personal records of minor and major happenings, many of them conjuring up pictures of the long ago. What service, I wondered, was Lieut. Colonel Anthony W. White engaged upon during the battle of Trenton, by which his horse strayed away. I even found myself wondering how the strawberry roan became rowelled in the breast. The occurrence certainly suggested a seat as awkward as uncomfortable.

$30.00 REWARD.

Strayed away the 28th day of June from the subscriber, near the field of battle, a strawberry roan horse, about 15 hands high. Has a very high carriage, trots rough, and frequently goes a rack. He has a blind brand on his near buttocks, a brown muzzle, a remarkable wart on the tip of his left ear, and has lately been rowelled on his breast. Any person taking up said horse and delivering him to Mr. R. Williams, tavern keeper at Trenton, shall receive the reward.

Anthony W. White,
Lieut. Col. L. D.

Following the brave Colonel White's appeal for his horse, Mr. Peter Hulick, of Trenton, had a neat announcement.

Peter Hulick, Staymaker of Trenton. Ladies by sending their length before and the width of the top and bottom may be comfortably fitted.

Next to Mr. Hulick's invitation to the ladies was a stallion announcement from Pluckamin, in the very heart of the present Essex Hunt Country, — in fact from the same village where hounds had met the day the Colonel and I hunted with them. I could but be impressed with the fact that one hundred fifty years ago a thoroughbred horse as large as sixteen hands had stood in that county and been described as an elegant and high bred hunter.

The ensuing season at Major Richard McDonald's, near Pluckamin, the elegant and high-bred hunter called "Ajax," full 16 hands high, moves well, for he walks, trots and canters as light as a pony. It is expected from the justness of his make and action that he will get fine horses.

The Colonel returned from wrestling with a long distance telephone call and remarked that we had certainly demonstrated the existence of horses in Colonial times, but that he wanted to look up some references to foxes and fox hunting which he had discovered in the index. I had not the slightest idea that fox hunting had assumed any great proportions in New Jersey in colonial days until the Colonel read the following letter from the Pennsylvania *Gazette*, but printed in the New Jersey Historical Records because it referred to that State.

FOX HUNTING — A LETTER FROM A JERSEY FARMER.

While America with the most laudable ardour is endeavoring to preserve her freedom, I am sorry to see so many of her sons like the foolish women pulling down with their hands the house the wise have built * * *, I address my Brethren Farmers and request their attention to a particular species of luxury that immediately

[94]

concerns us. I mean Fox Hunting, which is got to such a surprising lead within these few years that it is becoming dangerous in some places for a man to think himself so much Master of his own lands as to attempt to hinder these freebooters from ravaging every part of it at their pleasure. As the law is explicit, what have we to blame but our own supineness for suffering ourselves to be treated like Vassals by Fox Hunters. Nor let any be deterred from showing their dislike to this domineering sport from a fear of being ridiculed and sneered at. For be assured you will have the applause of the virtuous, the wise and the prudent, and the sneers of them who are galloping merrily on in the highways to destruction are not worth a thought.

(Signed) A New Jersey Farmer.

Some two weeks later a fellow farmer took up the defense of fox hunting, as farmers have done in all ages:

Messrs. Hall & Sellers,
Publishers Pennsylvania Gazette.
Gentlemen:

I am an aged farmer man who have enjoyed much good living in my time for which I acknowledge myself indebted to the city markets for enabling me to procure not as a purchaser, but as a seller. * * *

When I reflect on this it makes my blood run cold that any Jersey farmer should have been so weak and shown himself such an ingrate as to have published a piece in the Newspaper against the amusement of Fox Hunting begrudging the young men the use of this diversion in our woods. Little has the man considered that this exercise by creating them a stomach to eat plentifully of the provisions they allow us to supply them with is an advantage.

While he obliges me to tell him that it will do more than pay for all the little injuries that they may do by accident in pursuit of these noxious animals. What surprises me also is the oddity of this man.

He calls Fox Hunting a luxury and then rails on these friends of ours * * *

Let me ask him how we should dispose of our Water Melons, if it were not for the assistance of Luxury. He certainly must know that they are of no kind of use as food.   (Signed) A New Jersey Farmer.

The Colonel sat ruminating upon these ancient letters. He was a great antiquarian at heart and enjoyed digging into the past. "Pendleton," he said, "those letters were printed in the Pennsylvania *Gazette*, Number 2144, of January 25th, 1770. Fox Hunting had become so popular, so much on people's minds in New Jersey that the press was apparently willing to donate any amount of space to the subject. That was in 1770, Pendleton. Why, God bless me, that was before Beckford wrote. Personally I don't believe they ever hunted what we would call a 'pack' of fox hounds in England much prior to 1725. And Pendleton, don't get the idea that these Jersey sportsmen chased grey foxes around Jersey swamps. Listen to this:"

FRYDAY, THE 15TH JANUARY, 1713.
At a Council held in Burlington the bill entitled an act for the encouraging the killing of wolves, panthers and

red foxes was read the second time and committed to the gentlemen of the Council or any five of them.

"Pendleton, the Council was not concerned with grey foxes but with red foxes, who must have been so numerous in 1713 as to have become a menace. Do you remember being brought up on the theory that the red fox was imported into the colonies from England and first planted on the eastern shore of Maryland?"

That the sporting colonists were heckled by the reform element was evidenced by the following:

On Saturday, December 12th, 1761, the House of Assembly of Nova Caesaria (New Jersey) met. His Excellency, Josiah Hardy, Esq., Captain General, Governor and Commander in Chief in and over the province, gave his assent to an act to effectually prevent horse racing in the Province of New Jersey.

The Colonel read a dozen or more notices of horse races and match races which indicated that horse racing was perhaps the Colony's most popular diversion. As the Colonel was skimming through these notices he stopped, then said, "Pendleton, on our way over to Far Hills, New Jersey, we passed through Morristown. Do you remember quite a large public square in the center of the town? Listen to this:"

To be run for round the course on Morris Town green on Tuesday, the fifth day of November, 1770, a silver tankard of the value of twenty pounds.

Free for any horse, mare or gelding not exceeding three quarters bred, carrying weight for age and blood. Three year olds, half blood to carry seven stone, the best

[97]

three two mile heats to win the plate. Two dollars and a half entrance or double at the post. The entrance to be run for next day.

"That," said the Colonel, "was a sportsman's event. They were running for plate only and did not ask that the entrance money be used to defray the cost of the plate. The Committee threw the entrance money in, to be run for the next day. Twenty pounds. That was a lot of money in those days. Pendleton, where do you suppose that old tankard went to? Wouldn't Harry Worcester Smith enjoy stumbling upon that trophy? I'll wager he'd ship it over to Far Hills and talk those chaps into putting it in competition again. 1770. Why that's as old as the St. Leger Stakes."

I was particularly impressed with the simple, unemotional style in which events were recorded. The two boys mentioned in the news item appealed to me.

April 1st, 1779. A gang of robbers made a raid into New Jersey and stole 20 horses from Pompton Plains. A group of young men gave chase recapturing eleven horses. Two boys followed the robbers all the way to Hobuck. There one of the boys went down a steep bank to the river where he saw a block house. Looking in he saw one of the robbers with a pistol in his hand and carbine on the table. Opening the door the boy shot the man dead. The shot brought soldiers. The two boys discharged their two pistols and carbine, upon which the soldiers dispersed, and the boys rode back to Pompton.

It was surprising to note that even as early as 1740 the superiority of Virginian and Maryland horses was recognized, for the conditions of over half the races read, "Open to any horse except those bred in Virginia and Maryland."

By all odds the most common advertisement was for horses which had strayed away. In at least eighty-five per cent. of cases "a sore back" was given as one of the distinguishing marks of these horses, indicating that the Colonials used very bad saddles, slouched in their saddles, or rode unconscionable long hours. I ventured the belief that the frequency with which horses seemed to stray out on the roads was probably due to the lack of suitable fencing in a new colony. "Not a bit of it, Pendleton, not a bit of it," sputtered the Colonel. "God bless me, these poor horses were popping out of every inclosure from Hobuck to Cape May to give their backs a chance to heal. The damn thing makes me boil. A hundred thousand horses trudging in the red clay roads of New Jersey with sore backs."

The Colonel went on thumbing the pages searching for an entry of interest and finally found something which engrossed him. He re-lit his pipe, read the article again, and looked over at me. Indignation at sore backs was a thing of the past. "Pendleton," he said, "this picture starts my imagination into motion."

Came to the plantation of the subscriber on the 4th instant a dark brown horse, 14 hands high, and a small brindled dog also came with him. The owner is desired to come, prove property, pay charges and take them away.

John Watson, Jr.,
of Nottingham, New Jersey.

[99]

"Pendleton, small brindled dogs don't as a rule stray away from their homes. No. When that horse wandered out on the highway at night and started out to see the world the little dog concerned himself in the matter and went along with the intent of keeping an eye on the horse and perhaps persuading him to return. I didn't notice this advertisement yesterday when I looked through the book, but I did see a notice somewhere to the effect that the horse and dog had been claimed by a minister, and that the travelers had wandered some eighty-one miles from home. Just picture, Pendleton, what that little dog went through on that eighty-one miles. The horse could feed and browse as he traveled but there is nothing sustaining to a small brindled dog in grass and weeds. The dog couldn't leave the horse lest he not locate him again, yet the dog had to explore countless rear yards and pantry entrances, generally on the run, to pick up a snack here and there. And think of all the towns and villages they passed through, the horse placid, secure, undisturbed, but the little dog attacked by every butcher's mongrel for eighty-one miles. Then they came to Mr. Watson's place in Nottingham, and that gentleman shut the horse in the barn. God bless me, Pendleton, but that faithful little dog must have heaved a sigh of relief when he heard the door close on that horse. I can see the dog stretching out in the sun on Mrs. Watson's back porch worrying a bit about things at home, his buried bones and his various little daily interests, but saying to himself, 'Well, thank God this skylarking is over'."

The Colonel's interest and sympathy were aroused by the case of William Hambleton.

IN THE COLONY OF NEW JERSEY

New Jersey — Perth Amboy
20 Pounds Reward.

A prisoner made his escape from Jonathan Hampton, Sheriff, viz: — William Hambleton, a lusty, ill favored, dirty, slouching butcher.

Jonathan Hampton,
Sheriff.

N. B. He went off with his son and daughter in a two wheeled cart much like himself for rigging.

The Colonel's interest was augmented by reason of our finding three further references to the butcher, for readers of the sheriff's notice kept reporting to the newspaper that they had seen the butcher from time to time as he traveled the entire state en route to Philadelphia.

The Colonel, beyond any man of my acquaintance, had the gift of story. Given a situation which interested and appealed to him he immediately conjured a complete story. The sheriff was a brazen, bullying politician of the worst order. As a public servant he had no license to characterize a prisoner as an ill favored, dirty, slouching butcher, nor refer to his two-wheeled cart in a derogatory manner. The Colonel resented the business. The butcher became a great, lusty, powerful, good natured, sport-loving, easy-going individual, and a devoted parent. Upon effecting his escape from the sheriff he located his horse, which the Colonel assured me was a lean, raking, quick-moving, flea-bitten grey mare, hitched her to a dashing two-wheeled cart — a high cart, the Colonel said it was — climbed upon the seat, chirped softly to the mare, and the two of them slipped through the dark Elizabethtown streets. He located his two children, woke them, told them to pull on their duds and come quickly and quietly. While they were dressing the Colonel assured me the butcher located a big hooker of rum for himself, went to a private cache, extracted a few pieces of eight, and off the three of them started across the colony to escape gaol and the sheriff. "God bless me, Pendleton," said the Colonel, "picture the feelings, the excitement, the emotions of these two little children aroused in the middle of the night, hoisted up to that high cart, knowing that their father was escaping the gaol. Bless me, but I envy that boy. To him his father was a great man." "But, Colonel," I remonstrated, "there is nothing in the notice to indicate that the children were young. It just says son and daughter." "Tommyrot, Pendleton, tommyrot. Escaping butchers don't take grown-up children with them. No, the girl was eleven, the boy was thirteen. Ring the bell, Pendleton. We need a whiskey and soda."

We turned to some notes about Princeton.

The Rev. Mr. President Finley having been initiated as President of the College at Prince Town on Oct. 2, thought fit to make an oration. The Composition was made up with such purity of diction; flowing and harmonious periods; the pronunciation so exact and elegant, that no one but so great a master of the Roman language could have effected it.

Nassau Hall — Prince Town in New Jersey on Monday, Sept. 29, 1757 — Aaron Burr, President of the College died. He was born in Fairfield, Conn. His education he had at Yale College which is in New Haven in Conn.

Penn. *Gazette* July 16, 1761.

Lottery of the College at Prince Town.

In order to enable the College to continue, the following lottery is presented.

10,000 tickets at 4 dollars or 40,000 dollars.

3,337 prizes.

6,663 blanks.

"Pendleton, I suppose having had its inception in a lottery explains the apparent difficulty Princeton experiences in seeing eye to eye with the Harvard puritans. The churches did the same thing."

The Penn. *Gazette* No. 1562.

Nov. 30 — 1758.

A lottery has been erected and will be drawn on Bills-Island for raising 1500 Pieces of Eight to be applied to the use and finishing of the Church of England in the City of New Brunswick in East New Jersey.

The lottery consists of 3500 tickets at four Pieces of Eight each, 1060 of which are to be fortunate.

The Church hopes that their attempt will not be thought singular as it is solely for the promotion and honor of religion and that it will meet with such encouragement as will enable them to effect their purpose of completing the church.

"And look at the next entry, Pendleton. One moment they are promoting the honor of religion, then they are dealing in slaves."

On board the Schooner Hannah lying in the River Delaware near Cooper's Ferry, a cargo of likely Negroes just imported in said Schooner direct from the coast of Guinea, on which I would be pleased to quote terms.

Joseph Griswold.

New York *Mercury* — Nov. 18, 1756.

Run away — a Negro wench named Molly. Three weeks out of small pox — bred in Bermuda.

Any person that will deliver said wench to the workhouse in Philadelphia shall have 20 shillings reward paid at the London Coffee House.

These old newspapers were replete with time tables and schedules of coaches and wagons. The journey from New York to Philadelphia was not one to be undertaken lightly. Mr. Butler seemed to have worked out the best route we read about.

From the New York *Mercury* June 13, 1757.
Philadelphia to New York.

John Butler with his wagon sets out on Tuesdays from the Sign of the death of the Fox in Strawberry Alley — Phil. and drives to Trenton Ferry, where Mr. Holman meets him and proceeds on Wednesday to Brunswick, and the passengers being shifted into a wagon of Mr. Fitzrandolph he takes them to the New Blazing Star the same day, where Rubin Fitzrandolph with a boat well fitted takes them to New York that night.

Passengers finding comfort and pleasure in this method of transportation may return in the same safe and elegant manner.

John Butler.

[104]

The Colonel closed the book. "Pendleton," he said, "it was thus our forebears carried on. From this sort of a start we have developed the United States. God bless me but we have done well in a hundred and fifty years.

"From Mr. Butler's 'Safe and Elegant Wagon' we have evolved the Pennsylvania Railroad, automobiles, transcontinental airways, and four-way cement highways.

"From racing around the Green at Morris Town has come Belmont Park.

"In place of 'the Negro wench Molly, three weeks out of small pox,' who ran away, we now have a race of young women who walk abroad in the height of fashion and who are as close in touch with the world as are you and me.

"From Mr. Hugg's famous horse Yorick who was made 'so neat and strong' we finally arrived at Man of War.

"It is a far cry from Nassau Hall with ten students to one of the loveliest campuses in the world.

"The cargo of likely Negroes laying in the schooner Hannah at Mr. Cook's Ferry were the fore runners of our great army of unskilled labor for whose children we now build million dollar high schools. It's a fine record Pendleton."

The Colonel announced that his throat was dusty from reading aloud so he requisitioned two glasses of Rhine Wine.

When these arrived he lifted his glass. "Pendleton, in spite of the unique theory of the two young ladies of Far Hills, I give you a toast to the horses of His Majesty's Colony of New Jersey who turned the first sod, built the first road, carried the first merchandise and walked stoically forward to the field of battle — their contribution to liberty, and who carried on the work of building a mighty nation.

"Pendleton, to all horses of the Colonies. I salute them."

[105]

CHAPTER VIII.

And the Second Is Like Unto It

HE rode up to me at the meet. "The Herr Secretary?" he asked, removing his ridiculous looking cap. "Please, I would like to be of the hunt. Only for today yet Herr Secretary."

He was an incongruous figure on a horse in his sheepskin coat and black trousers tucked into the tops of a pair of high lumberman's shoes. His hands were encased in new bright yellow gloves with imitation fur at the wrists, — such as are sold to teamsters at country stores. A long, shiny black whip, reminiscent of toy shop windows, hung suspended from his left forearm.

He was of a squat, thick build, with a shaggy, unkempt beard which seemed to cover the greater part of his face. Above the beard sat a dull brown cap with an exaggerated visor and a length of tape around the crown, the purpose of which I did not grasp.

As I was surveying him, Colonel Weatherford, the Master, rode up with hounds. The man turned to me with a glow in his mild blue eyes. "The Herr Mastor?" he enquired anxiously. I nodded. Weatherford drew nearer. The man straightened himself, assumed a military position, and removed his cap. I saw a questioning look pass over the Colonel's face. He surveyed the visitor from head to foot, acknowledged the salute, and rode on.

It would be a long, exhausting task to do justice to the extent to which this man irritated and annoyed the members of the Millbeck Hunt that day. But in fairness to my old friends I plead that their irritation was well founded. The man exercised absolutely no control over his horse. He gave no indication of being sensible of having a horse under him. He climbed on the heels of other horses. He crossed in front of us as we galloped to our fences, endangering our very lives. He twice fell off, necessitating the catching of his horse. His mount stepped on Enid Ashleys horse's hind shoe, twisting and pulling it off so that Enid lost her day's sport. As his final act of devastation he bowled over an exceedingly good hound which was coming in from a wood-ride. It costs a great deal of money to support horses and hounds and all the paraphernalia that goes with a hunt, and when all is said and done those who furnish the sinews are entitled to pursue their sport in some measure of peace and security.

As ill luck would have it, we found a twisting fox in Three Spires Uplands. He doubled and turned and refused to leave the covert, necessitating our galloping up the wood-rides, harking, then, as hounds turned, galloping down again. It is a tremendous covert, and we must have done this half a dozen times, for you dare not let hounds get out of hearing in those woods and every time Colonel Weatherford passed us seeking his place at the head of the hunt the stranger would quickly assume his rigid military seat and remove his cap.

At the end of one of these fruitless pilgrimages the Colonel beckoned to me. I rode over to him. "Pendleton," he said, "if that Bolshevik looking rascal doesn't stop saluting me I will take hounds home." He sat harking to the hounds and glaring straight ahead of him for some time, then turned, and pointing at me with his crop, said, " 'and the second is like unto it. Love thy neighbor as thy self. On these two commandments hang all the law and the prophets.' God bless my soul, Pendleton, it's just this sort of impossible precept which deters a large part of mankind from paying attention to any precepts. It's all damned tommyrot asking people to do the impossible." Hounds turned just below us and again essayed the ridge. The Colonel spun his horse around and jogged off.

Our fox finally broke covert and laid a brilliant course for the foot of Smithboro Hill, with hounds on his back. For thirty exhilarating minutes of a rare, fresh fall day we galloped over one of the fairest lands in Christendom. Then, thinking of his home covert, the fox made a great loop and headed back for Three Spires Uplands.

I was going fast up front with Colonel Weatherford when far off to our right we saw a riderless, galloping horse. If you have hunted all your life, a riderless horse raises a question in your mind; has anyone been hurt? I saw the Colonel looking towards the horse. It was too far off to be recognized. Then we came upon them. The uncouth stranger had her in his arms carrying her across the great upland sheep pasture that runs from Three Spires Hill to Wendover.

The Colonel turned in his saddle, called to the field to go on with hounds, and he and I galloped towards the man. Colonel Weatherford fairly hurled his huge frame to the ground, handed me the reins and strode over to the man. "Here, hand Miss Sedgwick to me, hand her to me. I will carry the child." The man stopped, stood erect, and looked at Colonel Weatherford with those mild blue eyes of his.

Something of grandeur touched him. "The Herr Mastor will permit me to carry the liebes Kind. I have knowledge of such things. I am a vatter many times yet and a docktor chemeest."

That man, a stranger, a foreigner, and uncouth-looking was holding in his arms perhaps the most precious thing in the world to John Weatherford. I have known the Colonel for many years and in all this time I seldom knew him to be crossed. His eyes narrowed just a hair's breadth and the two men looked at each other; then the Colonel turned, reached for his horse, and we walked on.

It was a long, trying walk over a very rough stretch of land, yet that squat, powerful German carried the child as a skilled nurse might cross a room with a fretful infant. Mary's eyes were closed and her face ghastly grey, but withal she looked comfortable in his arms, almost as one in a gentle sleep.

Upon reaching the road we found the Colonel's groom standing there with the second horse. The Colonel called him. "Walsh," he said, "get these horses home, and there is another one tied somewhere out at the far end of that sheep pasture, and Miss Mary's horse is running loose. Get someone to help you and get them all home to my stable."

A car came by and we flagged it. "Herr Mastor," said the man, "you will hold the Fräulein, I will myself in the behind seat get. You will hand the liebes Kind to me mit care. You and the Herr Secretary will in the front be." Rebelling inwardly, and within a hair's breadth of exploding, the Colonel complied. As soon as we had started the Colonel turned to the man. "Do you know whether the child is dangerously hurt?"

"Nein, nein, Herr Mastor, nein. I listened to the heart when I was there yet with the sheeps. It is fine yet. The pulse, ach, it is beautiful. I count. Nein, Herr Mastor, the Fräulein, she will be well yet as soon she come to her mooter. The mooter, she will know what to do." It was very odd, but from the moment I first came upon the man with Mary in his arms a feeling of security and assurance came over me.

Upon reaching the house I went ahead to prepare Mrs. Sedgwick. The man handed Mary to the Colonel to hold, but, out of the car, immediately took her from him and carried her up the stairs to where Mrs. Sedgwick was waiting.

We three sat in embarrassed silence awaiting the doctor's verdict. Presently Mrs. Sedgwick entered in search of something. She is a rare person in her composure and dignity and understanding of all things. The man never took his eyes from her during all the time she was in the room. When she had left he moved his chair closer to Colonel Weatherford. He had taken off his sheepskin jacket and appeared in a tight fitting black coat of a most unusual cut, bedecked here and there with black braid. He sat on the very edge of his chair, suddenly pointed his finger at Colonel Weatherford and shook it at him a number of times, a liberty I had never seen taken before. "Herr Mastor, if the Virgin Mary had not been such a kind of a Mooter maybe Jesus Christ would not have been the same man yet."

The Colonel looked at the man for some time, then stood up, moved his chair over directly in front of him, sat down, leaned forward, and tapped the man's knee, saying, "Tell me, why did you want to come fox hunting today? Did you enjoy it? Did you get anything out of it?" A smile passed over the man's face; a really lovely, gentle smile that had its inception in the heart. "Herr Mastor, I am a moosician. I am a docktor chemeest, but first am I a moosician. Herr Mastor, everythings are mooseek — the great city, the quiet country, the water when she moves, the machine when it goes, all are mooseek. But Herr Mastor, three great mooseeks there are. First one is when kleine Kinder play in happiness — the laugh, the quiet voices, the clapping of the hands, one time excited, one time so soft. That is the mooseek of the world when she is growing up.

"Second yet is the mooseek of the chase. That is an old mooseek, Herr Mastor. It tells the story of when mens must hunt; when all things must hunt for their liebes Kinder.

"The last mooseek is the greatest mooseek of the world, Herr Mastor. It is men marching when it is the war. Four years I am of the war. The tramp of men's feet in the night; the wheels of gun carriages on the hard roads, the Herr officer's voice when he makes the command far away. That is the great mooseek of all the world; men going to death.

"Two mooseeks I know — the world growing up like when kleine Kinder play, and the world going down like when men march to war. The chase mooseek I do not know so good yet.

"Herr Mastor, two times I come to Millbeck and stay at Frau Holfstetter's boarding house. I am a shooter. I come to shoot the birds, and every time, Herr Mastor, when I come I see the hunt; the red coats, the many dogs, the horses, the Herr Huntsman. I hear the horses galloping, and the great calling of the dogs and the horn. A long time yet I listen to these things. Many miles I hurry to hear the mooseek. Voonderful it is, Herr Mastor, when one hound waits for the other to make the cry. Does the Herr Mastor think all the hounds make the cry together? Nein, nein, Herr Mastor. The birds, the crickets, the frogs, the hounds in the chase, all things that make mooseek must keep the time. I am a moosician. I am the first violin. Today I ask the Herr Secretary can I please be of the hunt for only one day yet so I know the chase mooseek. Six times yet Herr Mastor have I instruction taken from the Herr Professor to make the horse yump. If he yump, Herr Mastor, I am but if he do not yump then sometimes I am not."

I don't know how much time elapsed. It might have been three years, perhaps four. It was the night before Thanksgiving. The telephone rang. "It is the Herr Secretary? Could I again yet be of the hunt tomorrow, please?"

The next morning I went over to the kennels and rode to the Meet with Colonel Weatherford, Will Madden, the Huntsman, and the hounds. Upon arriving at the fixture it was evident that something untoward had happened. Then Clement Hastings rode up to the Colonel. He is a spoiled, over-bearing, dictatorial individual who sends four beautifully bred and schooled horses to Millbeck each season, — and then rarely comes to hunt them.

"Weatherford," he said, "I protest against that man over there riding with this Hunt. I protest against his hunting at all. That hired horse of his is not fit to be around other horses. It has kicked three horses already, including my own. What's the sense of a man having a red ribbon on his horse's tail as a warning that it kicks and then letting it wander all over the place kicking everybody in sight. I subscribe fifteen hundred dollars a year to this Hunt and I protest against that man riding."

Hastings was sorely disgruntled, but then his intriguing brown thoroughbred mare did have a welt on her side the size of a small saucer.

Standing in the middle of the road entirely deserted by the members of the Hunt who were, with just cause, giving him the widest possible berth, stood our visitor. The man's face was wreathed in unhappiness, bewilderment and anxiety. He had heard all that Hastings said, as had the rest of the field.

Hastings rode off, while the Colonel, a very great stickler for propriety in the hunting field, stood quietly in the center of the road looking at the visitor. Memory has an odd little way of recalling things to one's mind. As I stood there watching this trying scene and wondering what was about to happen, the Colonel's words came back to me, "And the second is like unto it." There were a hundred pairs of eyes fixed on John Weatherford. Suddenly I saw him touch his horse lightly with his heel and ride forward. The man in the road watched his approach with evident concern and embarrassment. When he reached the man the Colonel stopped his horse, removed his velvet cap with his right hand, transferred it to his left, in which he held his reins, reached out his hand, and I heard him say in a crisp, hearty voice that all could hear. "Herr Mueller, I make you welcome, Sir. It is a pleasure to see you out with us again. I hope you will dine with me this Thanksgiving day."

There was the same military squaring of the shoulders and the removing of the old brown cap.

The Colonel looked slowly over the entire field. He was apparently in quest of someone. Then he stood up in his stirrups and I saw him signalling with his crop. A groom rode up on the Colonel's second horse. "Walsh, Mr. Mueller will hunt my horse today. You will exchange with him. Madden, take hounds into the first covert."

Too many Thanksgiving evenings have come and gone for me to remember all the people who dined with Colonel Weatherford that night. George and Enid Ashley were there, and old Madam Estey, Henry and Edith Newcombe, the Reverend Huntington Sedgwick, Mrs. Sedgwick, and Mary. Then there was that old British war horse, Sir Charles Graham-Pierce, who was visiting the Newcombes, and I recall a Belgian baron. His name has escaped me, but he was one of the great archaeologists of his day, and was visiting Colonel Weatherford. The others have been lost in the clouds of old memories.

It was a pleasant gathering of friends and neighbors with many interests and affections in common; the hills of Dutchess County, the hounds that raced across them, and the foxes that bred and lived on their sunny slopes.

To the casual observer the glint showing back of Sir Charles' monocle as he appraised Herr Mueller's sartorial ensemble might have appeared a trifle flinty. But I knew it was only mild surprise for I had once taken a famous British general to view Niagara Falls and he had had the same look as he remarked that the Falls were rather unusual. Madam Estey was the only one perplexed, but that's because she still believed in certain things.

In this present era which sees the renewed abundance of the mediocre in vintages I look back upon the wine of that evening as did the ancients upon the flesh pots of Egypt. "Not now any more, in Europe, Monsieur, not in any place is one honored with such wine." Thus my Belgian neighbor at dinner confided to me with reverence and some emotion in his voice.

Shortly after dinner I missed Colonel Weatherford and Herr Mueller. Glancing towards the hall I saw them in earnest converse, the German with his hands extended in a suppliant attitude as though trying to dissuade the Colonel from some project.

When we were at last all reassembled in the library the Colonel's servant entered the room and handed Herr Mueller a violin case. Formerly of black leather, it was now a dull grey. In place of conventional metal clasps, which had long since disappeared, the case was held together by a length of black braid.

Colonel Weatherford crossed the room, stood with his back to the fireplace, and said, "We had a very good Thanksgiving run today. Hounds ran brilliantly, and we were in a galloping country. It was my pleasure to mount my friend, Otto Fritz Mueller. Mr. Mueller confesses to limited prowess as a horseman, yet has mastered a cardinal objective. He knows enough to let a seasoned horse alone. Because of this he witnessed and enjoyed all that our day's sport had to offer.

"Riding home he told me of having spent some years in endeavoring to portray in music that which a musician hears when he rides to hounds. This is Thanksgiving evening, a friendly, mellow occasion, and I have importuned Mr. Mueller to give the pleasure of hearing his composition to an audience which should be peculiarly appreciative of such music. Herr Mueller."

As I have confessed before, time has obliterated much of that evening, but nothing will dim my picture of Otto Fritz Mueller — his bulging figure, his odd garments, his topsy-turvy beard, his necktie high behind and failing of its principal function in front. But these were of no moment. The man's gentle, kindly smile, the blue of his eyes, the reverent touch of the old violin, his modesty and hesitancy, — these were things of the very man himself.

Twice he lifted the violin preparatory to playing and twice lowered it, looking earnestly over at Colonel Weatherford. "Please, Herr Mastor, would you say something yet to the people what it is the music tells, please." The Colonel shook his head. "No, Herr Mueller. It will not be necessary to tell them. The music will tell them."

The player seemed not convinced. He looked about the room in a perplexed, troubled air, then said, "Please, it is early morning yet of the hunt day. By the kennels every things are asleep already still."

A soft, dreamy note stole across the room evolving slowly into a gentle lullaby, and I found myself picturing the hounds stretched out on their benches, the Hunt horses in commodious, well-bedded stalls, Will Madden, the Huntsman, and his staff tucked away in snug cottages. Even the kennel cat came to my mind, asleep in a corner of the cook room. The music played on and the Millbeck Hunt slept.

Then a more alert note reached me and I knew that a hound had awakened, stretched himself, left the long bench and whimpered. The instrument suddenly broke into clamorous, vibrating strains, and I saw forty couple of anxious, expectant hounds crowding out into the yard to greet the morning. The kennels were awake. Another hunting day had dawned in Dutchess County.

When the first clamorous cry of hounds had subsided, a busy note of countless comings and goings filled the score, hurried foot-steps between oat bin and stall, the sissing of grooms doing up their horses, the clink of stirrup irons, water splashing into pails. Life at a hunt stable was being unfolded to us.

Again the clamorous cry of hounds. They were being re-leased. Thongs cracked. Will Madden blew three sharp notes on his horn, then the rap-a-tap-tap of the Hunt horses on the hard road, and when at times the music grew very soft we heard hound pads scuffling along.

I was picturing them jogging on to the Meet by Andrew Haightman's farm — a scene I knew so well, when again the music changed. There was a clatter of many horses and the talk of people. Hounds had arrived at the meet. Presently the field jogged slowly down the road. Then the music faded almost away, for hounds had entered covert, and we heard their soft pads on dry, crinkly leaves, and listened to the breeze blowing through oak branches. It was very still in the room, the music hardly audible. Then a new note, one not heard before, — a hound's voice speaking in covert on a fall morning. The player lowered his violin to his side. He waited. We all waited. The room was hushed. A hound had spoken. I did not see the violin lifted, but suddenly the room to its deepest niches was filled with music. Hounds had found. The covert rang with anxious cry. We heard hounds flying toward us, then away from us. The violin gradually softened. They had reached the far edge of the covert. The music sank almost to a whisper. Then we heard the Hunts-man's horse, and the strong rustle of other horses' feet in the leaves. The notes of the violin came so fast they crowded one upon another. Little Mary Sedgwick moved far forward on the couch and took my arm. We knew that hounds had

"Horses sweated and strained—"

reached the open and that the field was with them. I felt the roar of the wind as one gallops into it, and heard the thud of horses' feet.

The man played on and on. I saw old Sir Charles sitting on the edge of his chair, his hands gripping its arms. We hunted that fox in the open, ran him into deep woods and down into quiet, mystic swales. We coursed him to the high hills of Dutchess County and through the swamps that lie at the foot of those hills. Horses sweated and strained, and those who rode them were grim and alert. But through all this great panorama of sport there was brought to us by the strings of the violin a light, soft note, which kept for ever harping in our ears. It was a refrain — a motive, a haunting thing ever repeating itself; I knew well what it was — the feathery touch of a fox pad on the ground. The player produced it by touching the strings with his finger. And as we listened and saw the scene with our mind's eye the beat of the fox pad grew gradually slower — slower yet louder, and ever more insistent. Slower, always slower. I saw Mary's right hand pressing against her forehead. Colonel Weatherford, who had been watching the player intently, took a step or two towards him. Suddenly a cry burst from the violin, an eerie, fateful cry. Little Mary Sedgwick pressed my arm. "Oh, Mr. Pendleton, they have viewed him, they have viewed him. They are running into him." The violin rose and fell with the swaying of the man's body. A great volume of music filled the room and swept on to the upper reaches of the house. Forrard, forrard, forrard! I heard Will Madden's voice, John Weatherford's voice. I heard the struggling, galloping horses and pressing hounds. Then Will's high, tense scream. "Have at him lads. Have at him. Have at him."

[119]

The music sank to a plaintive, somber key, gradually fading into nothingness, and then Herr Mueller bowed.

Colonel Weatherford remained standing, evidently turning some project over in his mind and appraising the feelings of those in the room. Finally he said, "You all witnessed an unfortunate and exceedingly regrettable incident at the Meet this morning, for which I would like to see amends made. I would also like to see the members of the Hunt record their appreciation of a brilliant musical achievement. I now move you the election of Herr Fritz Mueller as an honorary member of the Hunt."

With the spell of the music still upon us we voted "aye, aye, aye." Old Madam Estey voted aye and clapped her hands. Sir Charles in his bluff way announced that although he had no vote the idea was top hole, top hole, and said bravo, bravo, in a voice that must have carried to the kennels.

We turned to look at Herr Mueller. He was making a series of stiff, formal little bows, his face wreathed in that contagious smile of his. He turned to Colonel Weatherford, saying, "Thank you, Herr Mastor, but I go back to Germany now. What I came to this country for is done. The chemeests every where now know of the things my uncle makes in Hamburg, so I go home. But Herr Mastor, I will accept the honor of a member being. I want very much I should be a member. My vatter, the Count von Bethwig und von Mueller will also much happiness get when I tell him I am a member of the hoont yet.

"Many times now will my vatter tell his friends, 'my son Fritz — he is a sportsman now. He makes his horse yoomp like in England.'

"Herr Mastor I go away in two days now but here is what

it is I wish, I wish the Millbeck hounds may have many years of good sport yet. That you, Herr Mastor, will ride always up in the front part — that the hoondts always will go faster and the foxes also. And when, Herr Mastor, you do not be in the front part, then next I wish Fräulein Sedgwick would be in the front part. All the ladies and gentlemens I thank."

CHAPTER IX.

The Hound Trial at Dykeman Center

The Hon. Mr. Arthur Pendleton,
Millbeck, New York.

Dear Sir:

I take pen in hand to ask if your honor will serve as one of the judges at the first annual hound trial of the Dykeman Center Fox Hunters Ass. to be held right here on Sat. Oct. 29th, and hope your honor will do it.

The meet will be at the green in front of my place, The O'Shannesy Arms Hotel, at eight o'clock, I mean in the morning. The dogs will be thrown in at Carey Swamp which is only a spell up the road.

The other judges will be Mr. Monahan from over the river, Judge McCall who runs his dogs near Hatfield, and Gen. John Winkleford, who is the master down your way. I am writing the other gents. today.

The fox hunters have put up a purse of $200 all to go to the winning dog. Rooms will be reserved for the judges at my hotel, the O'Shannesy Arms. Horses and stock saddles will be supplied.

There will be a banquet at the O'Shannesy Arms, my hotel, at six o'clock, so as we can present the purse, followed by a bang up dance and euchre at the Town Hall

(Slemps band from over to Hatzburg). Everything will be free for the judges, I mean banquet, dancing, liquor and such, please let me hear from you quick.

Resp.

Thomas Darcey O'Shannesy,
Mayor of Dykeman Center.

P.S.: I expect the bath tub will be rigged up in the O'Shannesy Arms (my hotel) then.

I don't suppose there was any one thing in the world that I felt surer of upon reading this letter than that I was not going to judge Mr. O'Shannesy's hound trial.

Dykeman Center is a small hill town lying some sixty-three miles northeast of Millbeck, reached by an atrocious road. A more unridable country does not exist up and down the Atlantic seaboard. The hills are high, steep, and rock-strewn, the low lands treacherous and often bottomless. A horse capable of navigating the walls has not yet been foaled, and an inaugural hound trial was bound to be an ill-organized affair. I had once ventured into this rocky fastness to purchase a herd of half-bred black Angus cattle from the estate of a deceased farmer, and recalled bumping up into the highlands over miles of narrow, rocky roads. And I also recalled with meager enthusiasm, the O'Shannesy Arms Hotel.

There is but one thing that can possibly be said in favor of Dykeman Center. It is the most natural and auspicious fox breeding and fox hunting country, for the unorganized type of the sport, within many hundreds of miles. The east branch of the Hadfield River winds its way to the west of the town in a series of gentle curves, and for generations the warm hill-sides making up from the river have fostered a stout race of foxes.

The Dykeman Center sportsmen breed their own hounds and run them over this stern countryside ten months of the year. They all subscribe to one or another of the old line fox hunting periodicals whose columns are chiefly devoted to long accounts of fox races had by fellow sportsmen in Missouri, Kentucky, Virginia and the Carolinas. It is meaty reading, of a cold, snow-bound winter's evening in Dykeman Center, to follow some fellow fox hunter running his favorite hound on the warm, sun-swept hills of the South.

It was therefore not to be wondered upon that Dykeman Center sportsmen should have wished to organize their own hound trial. This, however, was no good reason why I should set forth into the outlying districts to judge the event, particularly as there was no end of competent judges nearer at hand who would have relished the task.

I had just commenced my note of regret to the Hon. Thomas Darcey O'Shannesy when in came Colonel Weatherford with his letter of invitation in his hand. "Now then, Pendleton. Now then," he announced, "we must help these people out. Fine things hound trials, worth twice as much as the average society race meet and ten times a horse show. We'll go up and judge the thing. I'll send Walsh over the day before with a couple of horses, and we'll spend the night at home and motor early in the morning, for I have no faith in O'Shannesy's bath tub."

My protests, arguments and warnings against the project were of no avail. In the end I succumbed in a thoroughly weak-kneed fashion.

On the afternoon of Friday, October twenty-eighth, I

watched with grave misgivings, the Colonel's horse-van roll out of my place carrying the Colonel's good horse, Athelstane, and my Jack Semple, to Dykeman Center.

For some reason or other the Colonel developed the notion that I might fail to stir myself at four A.M. of a smart October morning or perhaps it was simply a case of misery loving company. In any event he proposed my spending the night with him.

We turned in about nine-thirty, and I immediately dropped to sleep. Insofar as I could gauge or fix the time, I gathered that I had been sleeping about half an hour when I was awakened by what sounded like people scuffling, wrestling or struggling. Some little ornament on the mantle in my room was tingling from the vibration. As soon as I could collect my wits I jumped up, hurried to the door, opened it, and listened. There was most certainly evidence of a struggle going on in a room further down the hall, and I could detect muffled voices. I hastened down the passage way, pushed open the door of a commodious combination dressing and bath room, and there, standing in the center of the room was John Weatherford, seriously engaged in performing a program of the most complicated exercises, and counting to himself in a gruff, determined manner. Hearing the door open he merely turned his head without interrupting the tempo of his gyrations. "Good man, Pendleton. Good man. Right on the dot. I'll be ready and down stairs in fifteen minutes. It's raining cats and dogs. I've been out to look at it."

Grateful for at least being now wide awake I dressed and hurried down stairs with the intent of exploring the larder on my own account, determined not to set out for Dykeman Center on only a snack of breakfast. The chance of getting any lunch was very remote and I had but little faith in Mr. O'Shannesy's breakfast.

Opening the dining room door I found very much to my surprise an animated, crackling fire in the hearth, a small table completely set, pulled up to the fire, and heard considerable bustling going on in the pantry beyond. Then the Colonel burst into the room rubbing his hands and aglow with that enthusiasm which a sporting expedition always aroused in him.

There are meals which so impress themselves on our memories that they become distinct high spots in our past. The fleeting years have added lustre to that morning's breakfast. I can't see the word omelette printed on a menu that my memory does not revert to the omelette of that morning, a kidney omelette, a kidney omelette the like of which few eyes have rested upon.

Omelettes were, I think, the principal gastronomic fetish of John Weatherford's household. The commodious rack above the kitchen table held at least a dozen long handled copper omelette pans of all conceivable sizes. The length of time an omelette should be cooked and the degrees of heat to which it should be exposed had been calculated to a nicety.

For as many years as I had known the Colonel his kitchen had been presided over by a Frenchman, Edouard, whom I probably would never have set eyes upon had it not been for the serving of omelettes. As soon as we sat down the pantry door opened, the white-capped Edouard stuck his head in the room. "Monsieur is now ready? I commence."

Coffee was poured. A padded contrivance, looking much like a small muskrat house, which, I found, sheltered a silver toast rack, was set on the table. Plates arrived heated to such a degree that they had to be placed on special straw mats; then the omelette, brown from end to end, delicately, evenly browned, was conveyed into the room by Edouard himself. The butler stood back. Colonel Weatherford surveyed the omelette. Edouard leaned over and surveyed it. Then they both studied it, after which the butler handed Colonel Weatherford a heavy silver dinner fork. Edouard stood with his hands clasped in front of him, his face wreathed in concern. The Colonel took the fork, laid it gently on the omelette, let it rest there of its own weight, and he and the butler studied it with breathless attention. The fork hesitated, then sank gently and easily downward. "Edouard, it is perfect, perfect." "Merci, Monsieur." The strain was over. Breakfast proceeded. A five o'clock autumn breakfast that still lingers on in my memory.

When we had finished we lit our pipes, bundled up against the storm, stepped into the car and headed over a series of narrow, rough, winding back roads for Dykeman Center. The wind had veered around to the northeast, driving penetrating splotches of rain before it.

Among the many things I will never be able to comprehend is how a man who has been but recently routed from a warm bed at an uncongenial hour can look out of a car window at a cold, grey, rain soaked country and wax eloquent about its charms. At the very first glint of light John Weatherford commenced peering out of the window and rubbing its surface in the hopes of increasing the visibility. "Look at that stone wall, Pendleton, four foot four if it's an inch. Clean as a hound's tooth, look at that take-off, perfect. God bless me, but wouldn't I like to kick a good horse into that wall — grand feeling when a horse pops his eye on one like that and begins to set himself and then jumps it clean. There is a lot of dishonesty about this jumping business, Pendleton. When a man's nerves begin to get a bit frayed he starts talking more and more about hound work, doesn't want a lot of big fences in the way. Says they interfere with getting on to hounds and that jumping bores him. He's a damn hypocrite, Pendleton. A big wall like that never bored anyone."

I said it was sixty-three miles to Dykeman Center. John Weatherford sat in his corner of the car and looked out of the window at every foot of the sixty-three miles. I verily believe he jumped every jumpable bar-way, stone wall and ditch. I believe he shot over every acre of stubble, poked in to every logical woodcock covert and cast a fly on every stream. I don't know how many times he demanded to know from Eugène where we were, and then scribbled some notation on his road map.

We arrived at the O'Shannesy Arms Hotel, a dreary, yellow building, from the unguttered eaves of which rain poured onto the muddy sidewalk, at seven-thirty. A somewhat slovenly young woman with her head done up in a dust cloth told us that Mr. O'Shannesy was entertaining in the private dining room and expecting us. We followed the young woman down a dark passage way from the far end of which came singing of a suspicious character, and were ushered into a small, low-ceilinged banquet room containing at that moment the cream of Dykeman Center's fox hunters and celebrities, some two-score in number. One fact was very self-evident. Whatever form of entertainment was now in progress had most certainly had its inception the evening before or perhaps even the afternoon before, and been carried on without interruption. There were empty and partly empty Green River

Rye bottles on literally every flat surface in the room.

Our entry brought forth a series of cheers, hurrahs and cat calls. His honor, Thomas Darcey O'Shannesy, large, expansive, jovial to a degree, welcomed us with so boisterous a cordiality, so great a hand-shaking and slapping of backs that Colonel Weatherford, with whom it never entered any sober man's head to take social liberties, fairly gulped with surprise.

Mr. O'Shannesy insisted upon first introducing us to our fellow judges, "Mr. Monahan from over the river," and "Judge McCall who runs his dogs over to Hadfield." Judge McCall was a short, round, bald little man of a gentle, benign expression. He was sitting at the head of the long table in a commodious leather arm chair, his hands folded complacently on his ample waist. To do the judge's sense of courtesy full justice be it said that he made a sincere effort to rise, a number of efforts in fact. The chair in which he was ensconced was extremely heavy and had been pulled up close to the table. The only way his Honor could hope to gain release was through planting his feet firmly against the lower round of the table and shoving with a will. This he attempted to do in good part, but having removed his shoes during some stage of the night his stockinged feet kept slipping off the lower round, and after each contest his Honor found himself materially lower in the chair. He finally waved us a cordial greeting and abandoned efforts which were as fatiguing as they were fruitless.

We turned our attention to Mr. Monahan. This gentleman, tall, sallow and gloomy, was standing by the fireplace, supported in part by its broad mantle on which his right arm rested. He started to take two or three steps towards us, thought better of it, and announced in deep, sepulchral tones "pleasedtameetcha," "pleasetomakeyouracquaintance." Judge McCall, apparently impressed with his compatriot's efforts, sang out, "Hurrah for Monahan. Monahan for ever." Upon which Mr. Monahan simply turned a pair of depressed, blood shot eyes upon the judge, but made no comment.

There were certain truths which could not be denied. Our fellow judges were not capable of functioning as such, certainly not on horseback. The fox hunters who had spent the night around Mr. O'Shannesy's board were not dressed or equipped to attend a hound trial, nor did they have their hounds with them, and finally it was a quarter before eight, and the green outside of the hotel was filling up with country people and their hounds.

Colonel Weatherford proceeded forthwith to expound these problems in no uncertain language to his Honor the mayor. Mr. O'Shannesy was masterful and efficient. Stepping out on his front porch he summoned all fox hunters within hearing distance and announced a half hour delay. He routed his guests out of the dining room and dispatched them to their several homes in quest of hounds, top boots and slickers, and announced to Judge McCall and "Mr. Monahan from over the river" that they were to do their judging from an automobile.

The Colonel and I located Walsh and our horses in a small, untidy stable at the rear of the O'Shannesy Arms. Walsh's appraisal of Dykeman Center, its people, hotel and stable, do not lend themselves to repetition.

Mr. O'Shannesy appeared in the stable yard, beckoned to a one-eyed, dejected looking individual who was leaning gloomily against a post, upon which the one-eyed man disappeared within the stable and led forth his Honor's mount, a stout, low-to-the-ground black horse, which was to tote the mayor's two hundred and forty pounds. We learned with some amazement that Mr. O'Shannesy was to serve as Master of Hounds. His only preparations for the hunt had been to tie the bottom of his trousers with stout cord to keep them from riding up, and to swing his cow horn over his shoulder. There was some little difficulty in getting the mayor mounted, which I will not touch upon because I have cherished through all these years a feeling of warm friendliness for the mayor. He was the political, social and sporting genius of this part of the world.

When all was ready we rode out of the stable yard, into the street and to the town green, the mayor in front and Colonel Weatherford and I just behind him, much in the manner of a personal body guard. There was some show of applause from those standing on the sidewalk which his Honor acknowledged by raising his huge grey felt hat.

Reaching the green the mayor unwound his horn and blew three reverberating blasts, then turned his horse towards Carey's Swamp and moved off down the main street.

I turned in my saddle and looked back at the long procession of mud-spattered cars, rickety buggies, men on foot, on horseback, on bicycles, and hounds of every size, type, breeding and color, with prominent numbers painted on their sides in yellow paint.

I venture to think that all residents of Dykeman Center who were not of the hunt were stationed on the main street standing in doorways or under the shelter of awnings. The mayor bowed right and left, acknowledging salutations from all quarters. At the corner of White Street a bus was discharging a group of school children. They cheered lustily. The mayor waved his hat, and blew a great blast on his horn. I caught the Colonel saying, "Well God bless my soul, what a business this is."

Carey's Swamp was a large, low-lying area covered with bushes, chiefly alders, but with patches of higher land here and there from which substantial portions of the swamp could be surveyed. The property was bounded on the south by scattered houses representing the outer fringes of the town; on the east by a long, thickly-wooded ridge, the steep sides of which bristled with grey stone cliffs. Towards the north the land rose towards limitless stretches of stone-strewn uplands. The west boundary was the road upon which our formidable cavalcade was aligned. To the west of the road lay a series of small, irregular shaped fields bedecked with out-croppings of grey rocks and fenced with very formidable stone walls.

There was an interminable delay occasioned by the non-appearance of the car conveying our associate judges. Proof was not lacking that these gentlemen had entered the car assigned to them and that the car had been at the green when the hunt assembled. The committee finally dispatched a young man back to the O'Shannesy Arms to reconnoitre. Some minutes later the machine conveying his Honor and Mr. Monahan from over the river drove up with a grand flourish. Judge McCall was still the bland, genial, smiling little person, sitting complacently back in the car, while Mr. Monahan glared morosely at the assembled fox hunters.

Hounds were to be cast in the swamp. Colonel Weatherford and I were to take stands on the high ground well towards the center of the area to be drawn, Judge McCall and

Mr. Monahan stationed their car on the west road, everyone being warned not to crowd or get in their way.

Mr. O'Shannesy, M. F. H., blew his horn, hounds were released and waved into the swamp, accompanied by that form of address which time had shown to be the most effective. Some hounds responded to endearing exhortations, others to varying degrees of profanity, while still others caught the point more quickly in response to a stout kick on the buttocks. One or two hounds fled into covert upon seeing their owners searching for stones.

Carey's Swamp had been hunted during all seasons of the year for the last hundred years, but never by more than a few couples of hounds at a time. On pleasant fall evenings three or four neighbors would assemble on the west road, release their hounds, and when a fox was on foot they would build a snug fire by the side of the road and listen for an hour or more to the cry, commenting in quiet, boastless country voices on the performances of the different hounds. A fox could not ask for better sport nor a higher degree of security than to weave his devious way through the vastness of Carey's Swamp at night with only three or four couples of hounds in pursuit. There had never been a kill in Carey's Swamp. But to cast fifty-one couple of hounds in the swamp at one time was bound to be disconcerting to any fox of fixed habits.

I poked Jack Semple through a gap in the fence, we threaded our way some distance into the morass and took our stand on a slight elevation. The ground had long been pastured to cattle and was honeycombed with paths and broad swaths which the cattle had cropped. Colonel Weatherford took his position some little distance from us. Hounds were ranging and trying on all sides of us.

The rain had been trickling down my neck for the last hour and I was on the point of tying a handkerchief tightly around the outside of my raincoat collar, when a hound, whose number I could not decipher, started to feather not twenty feet from me. I had noticed this particular hound both at the town green and while waiting on the west road. He was an extremely large, well turned, black-backed individual with a determined, independent air about him, the sort which get keener the longer they run and at the end are ready and able to break a fox up single-handed. His stern was becoming increasingly active but as yet he had not opened. A fox had undoubtedly crossed over the ground some time that morning.

The hound felt for the line among every blade of grass, stone and bush, but could not be sure. He tried for it at the four points of the compass, then finally raised his head and looked up at me as though inquiring whether I could contribute a clue. He then stood perfectly quiet looking over the terrain. Hounds have good and sufficient reason for every move they make. This hound had exhausted all the resources of his nose and could make nothing of the line, so he was simply standing there using his eyes in an effort to determine where the fox might possibly have gone.

After standing thus for perhaps a minute he walked over to a clump of low bushes and pushed his way through them to a small clearing. His head went down and almost immediately he whimpered softly and his stern became violently active. At this point a hound at the far corner of the swamp opened with a crisp, keen note. A score of hounds honored. The black-backed hound spun around, stood a moment with his near foot raised, then returned to his own line.

At the fringe of the clearing he struck the scent in earnest and opened with a voice which sounded exactly as I had expected. Three hounds near us flew to him and I could hear others splashing through the swamp from all directions.

Having noted the several hounds as they honored I moved slowly on. Colonel Weatherford joined me and I pointed out the hound which had first hit the line. The cry which we had heard at the far corner of the swamp had increased in volume. Whether these distant hounds had unkenneled a fox of their own or had hit the line of our fox was difficult to tell. Our own line was exceedingly twisty and apparently not too fresh, which afforded us countless opportunities of observing hounds work, and whenever we caught a glimpse of them the big black-backed hound was clearly dominating the situation. After observing him a few times the Colonel formulated designs for taking him back to Millbeck.

At the end of about fifteen minutes the scent improved. Hounds' voices became stronger, and the pace quickened. It became increasingly difficult for us to stay with hounds, for the incessant rain was fast making the swamp unridable. We had twice come within an inch of getting bogged, and Jack Semple was thoroughly distrustful of the entire terrain.

The picture was suddenly and alarmingly changed by hearing our hounds far over towards the north fringe of the swamp. From the intensity and shrillness of their cry one would almost have thought that they were running into their fox. The balance of the hounds were over towards the center of the covert, a section we could not reach due to the going. The time had clearly come for action. An automobile horn sounded out on the west road, whether by accident or as a hint to us we did not know.

The Colonel had been smoking his pipe with a perforated metal cap affixed to the bowl to keep out some of the rain. He rapidly emptied the pipe, squared his shoulders, clucked to old Athelstane, proclaimed his satisfaction at not having a large family of undernourished children dependent on him, and we forged across the swamp towards the north.

Had I been alone I could and would have picked and poked my way across that swamp with some measure of comfort and reasonable security. As it was I floundered through it in the wake of John Weatherford at a pace that made the event a nightmare for months afterwards. I can feel Jack Semple under me to this day, his head far down and out in front of him, jumping, straining, twisting, lurching from hillock to hillock, steam rising from every pore, and grey oozy mud engulfing his hocks at every stride.

We came at last to the boundary fence separating the swamp from the broad fields beyond. It was a great, rough wall ditched on the take-off to drain the water down to the sluggish stream which meandered through the swamp. In front of the drain was a deeply rutted, rocky lane, the ruts of which were now flowing with water. The Colonel plowed on to the fence looking neither to the right or left, leaving the situation largely up to his horse, in whom, after nine seasons, he had explicit faith. Athelstane, who thoroughly understood that his task was to jump that wall with all its foreground, and above all to keep on his feet, took off at the very fringe of the lane and was a foot over the wall. Little Jack Semple, who is only a mite of a horse, made more to do, but carried me boldly, landed safely, and immediately started fighting for his head in celebration of having survived the swamp.

We were now in an apparently limitless rock-strewn field galloping due north on the line of hounds, the last of which we had just seen disappearing over the hill in front of us.

Looking back and over towards the west I could still see the fox hunters huddled on the road, apparently intent on what was going on in the swamp. Off by itself stood the judge's car with Mr. Monahan from over the river and his companion perched on the roof, perilous, I thought, in their then condition but nothing comparable to following John Weatherford across an uncharted country in the teeth of a northeaster. I confess, even at the risk of being thought a bit faint-hearted, that during the first few moments of that run my mind kept continually reverting to Millbeck, to my library, my genial hearth, to the friendly games of bridge that would be in progress, to people curled up in front of cheerful fires with books. I even persuaded myself that my setters, snoozing on their bench, were much better off.

The temptation to write an Odyssey of that run is very strong. It lends itself to descriptive narrative beyond any event that has ever befallen me or ever will, but all minute accounts of spectacular events fail of their purpose.

In spite of having ridden and hunted since infancy in a county difficult and exacting on hounds, foxes, horses and those who ride them, I don't think I ever quite comprehended until that day what hounds, foxes and horses could endure. For exactly four hours and sixteen minutes from the time we left Carey's Swamp we followed the greatest running, the most persistent, — certainly the most enduring fox I ever saw in front of a pack of hounds. How far we ran him, or where we ran him I will never know. In the course of the day I looked down upon eleven different villages and hamlets. I rode Jack Semple through places and over obstacles I had never believed navigable for a mounted horse. In my present less adventurous age I actually and positively shrink from the contemplation of certain events of that day. I recall skirting a long, wire-strewn stone wall, a wall of tremendous proportions, and hearing John Weatherford's glee when he discovered what he insisted upon terming a breach in the wall. True the wall had broken down at this point so that it stood not above three feet, and was free from wire, but a dilapidated farm wagon minus a front wheel had been lodged in the gap. A mass of loose rocks lay strewn on the take-off side, requiring a horse to stand off from the fence an unconscionable distance. The Colonel insisted that the wagon was frail and would probably crumble if we landed on it or in it, a surmise which brought me cold comfort. I still retain a vivid picture of the Colonel essaying that obstacle and of Athelstane fighting to keep from dropping his hindquarters into the wagon, and I can also feel the power and determination which little Jack Semple put into his jump.

I recall standing beside the Colonel in front of a low stone wall and peering down over it to a slippery stretch of concrete road some ten feet below. The Colonel dismounted, threw the reins over his horse's head, tied the end of his thong to the reins, asked me to hold his horse, climbed over the wall, and floundered down the wet yellow clay bank. When he had traveled as far as the end of his crop would permit he told me to turn the horse loose and neither to speak to him or encourage him. The Colonel gave the rein a light twitch. Old Athelstane was standing not above a foot from the wall looking down at the road in distrust. Feeling the signal from the reins he took another long survey, raised back on his hocks, jumped as conservatively as it seemed humanly possible for a seventeen-hand horse to jump. There was not above three feet of level ground on the landing side but he managed to connect with this narrow strip with his hind feet, steady himself, and then slide down the embankment on his tail. The Colonel tied him to a tree and then plowed up through the clay to hold Jack Semple for me.

Time upon time that day I was forced to stand that game little horse of mine with his chest practically resting against stout, formidable walls, and ask him to jump into impenetrable brush, woods and tangles of grapevines. So dense was the growth in those woods that it was impossible to give a horse even the advantage of a single stride. I rode him down hillsides so steep and slippery I would have thought them suitable for only mountain goats.

Our fox explored the secret recesses of every swamp, large and small, in that part of the county, and no hill seemed too steep provided it lay in his line of flight.

Towards the middle of the afternoon the Colonel insisted he could see the State Capitol at Albany, and towards the end of the afternoon he alleged emphatically that he could distinguish the American end of the Suspension Bridge across the Niagara River.

I doubt whether judges of a hound trial ever enjoyed more opportunities of viewing, scoring and appraising hound work than did we that afternoon. For my part I filled a note book. Every hound in that pack became a distinct individual. We knew many of them as thoroughly as our own hounds at home. We studied them as they entered one swamp after another, listened to their cry, and compared their order on coming out. We saw them lose and find and lose again, times beyond count, and through it all, from the beginning to the very end, the black-backed hound was supreme. Of all hounds I ever saw run a fox he was the most relentless. Nothing stopped him, nothing distracted him. He never deigned to crawl under or through a fence, but went over the top. I listened to him in the wet, heavy, treacherous going of the swamps, throwing his tongue right and left and driving on. He came out of swamp after swamp often a hundred yards in front of the rest of the pack. When scent failed he would make great, wide, independent casts to the four points of the compass and before most hounds knew what was going on, he had hit the line and was flying forward. He was of the material of which great champions are made. A fitting hound to run that particular fox.

As the day began to ebb we pulled up a long, gradual slope to a series of bleak, wind-swept pastures extending as far as the eye could see. The wind increased and the rain came in vicious gusts. We pioneered over a series of very formidable walls to be finally brought up short by a jump over a stout slat fence down into a narrow lane. The fence in itself was high enough to cause one to hesitate, but when to this was added a terrific drop into a rutty stone-strewn lane, the problem became acute. The Colonel surveyed the situation, irritated and exasperated. "God bless me, Pendleton, if I don't think I'm stumped. If this horse lands in the lane on his feet he can't jump out of it. He can't land flat-footed and stop dead in his tracks. I think he'll stand on his head. He's too big for such a situation. What are you going to do?" While I was considering the problem the Colonel touched me with his crop "Look man, look." I turned. The hunted fox was recrossing the lane some distance to our left. He had evidently turned, made a loop and was retracing his steps. A more beaten fox I never looked upon. His brush was dragging and bedraggled — his head down and tongue lolling out of the side of his mouth. He would trot a few feet, then walk with a rolling, lumbering gait. He had evidently overrun the place he was searching for. We looked on beyond him and saw a series of low, rock ledges, some half a mile away. "He knows an earth in those ledges, Pendleton," said the Colonel. "I hope he makes them. Bless me, if I wouldn't like to help him." We walked our horses slowly in the wake of the beaten fox. Hounds' voices were coming steadily nearer. The fox heard them and set his ears far back. "Damn it, Pendleton, it doesn't seem fair for us to take sides and cheat twenty couple of hounds who have done what this pack has done." I could now distinguish the black-backed hound's keen, relentless cry and turned just in time to see him coming over the top of the slat fence a yard or two below where the weary, laboring fox crawled through. "A sinking fox has little scent, Pendleton." I knew on whose side the Colonel stood. The black-backed hound faltered a moment some twenty feet beyond the fence. By going over the top he had gone too far out into the field, for the fox had snuggled the fence row. The hound made one quick cast forward, then turned, flew back to the fence, hit the line and came flying toward us. I turned and looked towards the ledges, then stood far up in my saddle. The Colonel pointed and I saw the fox. He was pulling up a slight incline. I saw the Colonel stand up in his stirrup, look back at the black-backed hound, then at the rest of the pack which were now crossing the lane, then on to the fox, and finally measure the distance to the ledges. The black-backed hound now reached us. He was running strongly but giving little

[142]

tongue. Scent was failing. He passed us and we started to jog
after him, the Colonel and I both standing in our stirrups.
Of a sudden the hound opened with a new, clamorous, fran-
tic cry. His head was up. He bounded forward. "He's viewed
him, Pendleton, he's viewed him." Pandemonium broke out
behind us. A lean, blue-ticked little bitch shot by us. We
kicked our horses into as near a canter as they had left in
them, standing as we rode. I focused my eye on the lowest of
the rock ledges. There was no way of telling where the earth
might be. The Colonel was a stride or two in front of me. I
saw him clout old Athelstane over the quarters. I suddenly
caught sight of the fox. The black-backed hound was not
above fifty feet from him and the Colonel not above four
strides back of the hound. Then the Colonel for some reason
cut in front of me and I lost sight of hound and fox. Suddenly I heard the Colonel shout "whoop, whoop, whoop."
"Have at him, have at him, have at him, lads. Whoop, whoop,
whoop. He went in, Pendleton. He's in. He's safe in, thank
God. Have at him, lads, have at him! Whoop, whoop,
whoop."

We dismounted and gathered hounds around us, that is as
much around us as one can ever gather a miscellaneous lot of
independent, trencher fed hounds. In the let-down which
followed so strenuous a day, the immediate future looked
dreary in the extreme. To begin with the Colonel propounded
the problem of how we were to announce the black-backed
hound as the winner if we could not designate him by number, name or owner. The chances of the hound following us
back to Dykeman Center were practically nil. The chances
were he would not follow us ten feet from the earth. He was
apt to start across country for his home, wherever that might

be, any moment. His number had been nothing more than a daub of yellow paint from the first time I noticed him. The Colonel removed a rein from his bridle and one from mine, tied them together, wound a handkerchief around the end and captured the hound by a subterfuge. A number of the hounds had already started to wander away.

We stood at the edge of the cliffs looking over the rain soaked and now darkening countryside in an effort to get our bearings. We were in accord in thinking that we belonged far to the south, and agreed as to where south might lie.

We mounted, called such hounds as might be companionably minded, and poked our way along in search of a road. I have referred to the persistency and determination of that great, black-backed hound. Every trait I admired in him while running the fox I now resented. He rebelled at being led. He resisted by every known artifice. The Colonel dismounted a score of times to reason with him, to humor him, to try and establish some friendly relationship. The hound would have none of him. In twenty-five years I never saw the Colonel in a more noble rôle. His patience seemed inexhaustible, and in view of the hour, the many miles that lay before us, and the cold, wet wind we were facing, there would have been just cause for the Colonel to have been a bit short of temper at such unreasonable obstinacy. He neither complained nor threatened, but finally said to me, "Pendleton, this hound resents this whole business, and I don't blame him. His feelings are hurt. His pride is hurt. He can't understand the thing. God bless me, I can't drag this hound back of me like a criminal. I would rather carry him. Here — hand him up to me." I don't know whether you have ever carried a large, rain-soaked, mud-bedraggled hound on horseback. But the

Colonel was a huge, rugged, powerful man, and he quickly evolved a method which promised some comfort for both the hound and himself. We agreed to take turns at stated intervals.

In due course we discerned a narrow, winding and but little used county road, and turned toward what we hoped would be Dykeman Center. Our affairs were not bettered by the fact that Athelstane had lost a front shoe and Jack Semple two rear shoes. At the end of some three-quarters of an hour, during which we had neither met anyone on the road nor seen a house, we came to a crossroad and a sign board announcing it to be eleven miles to Dykeman Center. Making no comment, we plugged stoically on.

I had just been relieved of the hound and was considering the possibility of perhaps dozing off when I heard the Colonel say, "Did you ever have lumbago, Pendleton?" "No," I answered. "Well, I have, and I'm going to have it again tomorrow if I don't get in by a fire for a few minutes. I'm going to stop at the first house we come to, and warm my back, provided there are any houses in this part of the world." I went on with my sheep counting or whatever method I had evoked to produce somnolence, and was half dozing when I felt Jack Semple come to a halt. I looked up and saw a light shining from a house window. The Colonel was contemplating the light with some misgivings.

We rode into the yard and looked about. The prospects were not hopeful. There had been a fire at the place, as evidenced by a bleak chimney, all that remained standing. The occupants had apparently taken up their abode in one end of a dilapidated stable, into which they had fitted a door and two windows. I dismounted, took the hound from Colonel

Weatherford, gave him my horse to hold, and knocked at the door. It was opened by a young woman, at the side of whom stood a boy of perhaps twelve or thirteen years of age, who assumed a protective attitude. Thinking that our appearance would no doubt prove alarming I hastened to explain that we simply wanted to get by a fire for a few minutes before continuing our journey to Dykeman Center. I need not have concerned myself about alarming that woman for the world had showered her with too many tribulations. She smiled and welcomed us with graciousness, and told her son to help us put away our horses. We followed the boy to a door at the other end of the barn, located a few odd lengths of rope which we joined as shanks, discovered a piece of thin, dilapidated carpet which we threw over Athelstane's loins, and an old carriage robe which did for Jack Semple. The Colonel would not leave the hound in the barn fearing he would escape, so he accompanied us.

When we reached the house the kettle was on to boil, and a rejuvenated fire crackled in the stove. The improvised house consisted of but one room, along each side of which stood a narrow cot. A diminutive cook stove nestled in one corner with a flimsy, crooked smoke-stack rambling out of a crude aperture in the wall. There was a rough board cup-board in the opposite corner which apparently held articles of food and the meager supply of cooking utensils. These things one took in and passed over at a glance. They were but the symbols of very abject poverty. It would have taken more time, very much more time then we had to spend to comprehend other things in that room, the woman herself most of all.

It seems strange to me, after all these years, that that woman's face should continue so hauntingly fixed in my memory. One would think her likeness would have become gradually amalgamated with all the countless other faces one meets during a decade or more. But whenever I hear French spoken she invariably slips softly across the stage of my memory. I see her standing in a rough barn room, her home, dressed in a crisply laundered blue and white checked gingham dress with a deep white turned-down collar and a large blue bow tie.

Her figure, her hair, the quick, tense, impetuous movements of her French race, these things savored more of girlhood than womanhood. In the original scheme of things it had been intended that she should laugh a great deal and be gay and shed gayness. Her eyes and mouth, the whole lovely mould of her face were designed with particular reference to laughter.

A small passing event would instantaneously ignite the torch of merriment, but when the light flickered out she seemed much as a child facing an unexplored danger. She looked at one questioningly and bewildered and as though silently asking what next. What will happen now? What can one do? Tell me what would you do? She labored bravely and painstakingly with the English language but you knew it imprisoned her thoughts.

She drew an unpainted kitchen chair up to the stove with its back towards the heat, looked at our two six-foot figures, pointed at a diminutive little rocker, the only other chair in the room, laughed a pair of appropriately placed and skillfully designed dimples into being, then removed a few toilet articles from an upturned box covered with a piece of old mellow red material, and moved it to the fire. "You will sit in the backward way first. It is better so," she said.

At her insistence we sat down with our wet backs close to the stove and our long mud-spattered legs stretching out into the center of the room and watched the preparations for tea.

I was just giving thanks for being out of the saddle and rain when the Colonel said, *"Madame, la fumée vous dé-range-t-elle?"* The woman was dexterously preparing some exceedingly thin slices of bread with a jack-knife blade. At the sound of her mother tongue spoken as her kith and kin would have spoken it, she fairly spun around on her heels, extended her outstretched hands to us. "Oh, *Monsieur*, please smoke. Have you everything? Pierre — matches for the gentlemen. Oh, it is so wonderful to hear Monsieur speak my language. *La belle France.*"

I don't know just how John Weatherford, in the space of only a few minutes gained the whole of the story. I suppose it was because he was large and paternal and kindly-looking and knew no inhibitions and was direct and took you off your guard, but probably chiefly because he was talking to a lonesome, forlorn, distraught, estranged little woman, and one who didn't want to grow up.

It was a very simple, humdrum, every day story. She had become enamoured, much against her family's wishes, of a young American who had been sent to Paris as a representative of a large machinery corporation. I gathered that the company's product had something or other to do with oil refinery equipment, but my French failed me when the beauties, efficiency and purposes of the "belle machine" were being enlarged upon, and even Colonel Weatherford scowled and jerked at his mustache as the voluble flow of French adjectives told us about making two gallons of perfect gasoline flow where one "poor, weak, miserable, watery, dreadful, wretched, inconsequential, impoverished gallon" flowed before, all because "of my husband's beautiful machine."

She was vague, intentionally so I thought, as to why her husband had lost his connection with the firm, but passed on to his failing health, their coming to America, the necessity of the man's living an outdoor life, their slim remaining resources being invested in a farm up among the rocks back of Dykeman Center, because it was cheap. She told of their struggles during two cold, lean years. "The crops *Monsieur* — we were too late or we were too early. It was too dry or it was too wet. The cows, they would not have their amours when it was the right time. The chickens, *Monsieur*, their thoughts were of admiration for the rooster, eating, taking a bath in the dust, strutting this way and that. They had no desire, *Monsieur*, for the laying of eggs."

Then came the husband's death, and finally on a Sunday morning when mother and son were in the village, the burning of the little house. The insurance money, not sufficient for the construction of a new house, had been collected by the mortgagee. There having been no insurance on the contents, mother and son found themselves in what looked to me as near destitution as I could well picture.

The insignia of tragedy is easier recognized than described and perhaps it is easier recognized in a pair of large, tense brown eyes surmounted by soft brown curls. Her moods changed with startling unexpectancy. One moment she was telling of the loss of her few little possessions, the rosary given to her by *"mon cher* Abbé Quintard." The sewing table, a Louis XIVth sewing table, a table with "millions and millions of little drawers and places for everything, *Monsieur*, a gift from her *grandpère*, the Chevalier Fronterac.

[149]

"*Ils ne restent plus, Monsieur,* and they were very beautiful." The next moment she clapped her hands and broke into a low and decidedly contagious laugh and pointed to a dark corner of the room where a parrot, which we had not noticed, was sitting like a sphinx on a small clothes press. "But Paul Jean Clemenceau, he survived, *Monsieur.* He was spending the day out on the apple tree. When we came home and everything was gone he was so cross, *Monsieur.* Oh, *Mon Dieu, Mon Dieu,* how he scolded me about his perch having been destroyed. Oh, *Monsieur,* such words he used *à grands cris.*"

During all this time the boy had been sitting on the floor in a corner of the room intently watching the black-backed hound, and now and again I would see him slip his hand back of the hound's ear and stroke it gently, and the hound's tail would tap the floor a time or two.

It surprised me that anyone could get a friendly response from that hound. The mother noticed me looking at the boy. "My little Pierre has great love for animals and has pretty ways with them," she said. "He, too, has a hound, a white hound, not so big, Monsieur, but very brave."

The boy rose to his feet and came over to Colonel Weatherford. "Is it *Monsieur's* hound?" "No, my boy," answered the Colonel. "I don't know who owns it but it is the best running fox hound I ever saw. It has won the Dykeman Center Trial today."

The boy took a quick step backward and stood looking intently at the Colonel. "Monsieur says this hound won the two hundred dollars. The two hundred dollars? This hound won it?" He turned and walked across the room and stood silently looking out of the window into the blackness. His mother was watching him and as she watched a look of pain crossed her face and she passed her hand over her forehead. She started to pour tea, when we heard a movement over by the window. The boy was crossing the room with quick, active steps. He bore a tense, drawn expression. The mother was evidently apprehensive, for she said, "*Pierre, mon petit, calme toi.*" He apparently did not hear her. When a foot or two from Colonel Weatherford he stopped and said, "Monsieur, that two hundred dollars would have bought the sewing machine for my mother. That hound won two hundred dollars. That would have bought the machine, then my mother could have lived like before. Does not the good God care, Monsieur?" "Pierre, Pierre, please, please do not say such things. These gentlemen are our guests. Please, my son."

The boy stood in the center of the room looking now at us and now at the black hound, then suddenly turned on his heel, crossed the room, opened the front door and went out into the storm. "*Monsieur* will please excuse my son. He is unhappy, but only for me, *Monsieur*. He is very brave for himself. When my husband died I became a seamstress." A ghost of a twinkle came into her eyes. "In this place I am a very good seamstress. Madam, the Mayor's wife, says I am very neat for a foreigner." The twinkle became gayer. Then it was gone. "The fire took my machine. *C'est fini.* How does Monsieur like his tea?"

The ride home seemed shorter than I had thought it could be. Perhaps my discomfiture seemed of less import. When we dismounted at the stable yard the Colonel removed his black derby hat, wiped his face with the large silk handkerchief which had done valiant service as an absorbent during that long, wet day, and looking over at me in a quizzical way, said, "Pendleton, this is a damned inexplicable world to me."

[151]

We delivered our leg-weary horses to Walsh, looked them over by the aid of a lantern, instructed Walsh to wait over an extra day before vanning back to Millbeck, and then made our way to the O'Shannesy Arms.

The banquet had reached the apple pie-and-cheese stage, and as we were being escorted to seats reserved for us to the right and left of Thomas Darcey O'Shannesy, M. F. H., we were greeted with cheers, pertinent questions and a gentle gibe or two at our expense, but withall with great good humor.

Colonel Weatherford, sensing that the guests were anxious to proceed to the "bang up dance and euchre party (Slemp's band from over to Hatzburg)" decided there and then to forestall his dinner and announce the award so that the purse might be presented. We had brought the black-backed hound into the hotel and given a small boy a coin to hold him securely out in the hallway. The Colonel signalled me to get the hound, which I did, and the hundred or more guests turned to look at us as I led the hound to the head of the table.

There have been few speeches or in fact oral performances of any kind which I wish might have been recorded so that I could at my pleasure re-hear them, but I would to this day give a great deal if I might again listen to John Weatherford's account of the prowess of that black-backed hound and the game fox he hunted. I marvelled then and ever will that an event, any event, could have made so detailed a photographic record on anyone's memory as did that run on the Colonel's memory.

He carried every fox hunter in that room over mile after mile of country. They saw the course of the fox and the difficulties of the hounds. They followed us over fences, over brooks, through swamps, onto the crests of great wind- and rain-swept hills, and in their mind's eyes was a slim, tawny rain-soaked fox far out in front, pursued by a determined, forward driving hound. A dozen times they banged on the table so that the dishes rattled, and when at the end, the Colonel, with his hands resting on the table and his huge body leaning far forward over the table, told as only a great story teller could have told, of the fox making his last supreme effort and dropping into the earth with the black-backed hound grabbing at his brush, — they rose to a man and cheered and waved their napkins and pounded each other on the back.

The Colonel waited for silence and then, with a memorable tribute to a really great hound, announced our decision, and raised his glass, "Mr. Master and gentlemen, I give you the winner. May he long run forrard on."

A more complete silence never hung over a gathering of people than hung over that room following that toast. I glanced over at the Colonel. He was looking around the diners, his face wreathed in perplexity. He fumbled for his glasses, popped them on his nose, studied the situation, but found no solution, so turned and looked down at Mr. O'Shannesy. I was also looking at the Mayor. His usually jovial face was flushed with what I could only construe as embarrassment. He rose to his feet, removed a napkin, a corner of which had been inserted in his collar, cleared his throat a number of times, then said, "General Winkleford, it seems like this hound trial didn't work out smooth and slick the way we planned her, not no which way. Here is how she is. You see when you and Mr. Pinkleton went out of the swamp with your fox you only had twenty-three couple of hounds with you. There isn't any doubt about that, General, because when the hounds you left in the swamp crossed the west road after *their* fox we counted them, twenty-eight couples of 'em, General."

I have spoken with enthusiasm about Colonel Weatherford's stirring account of our great run. Mr. O'Shannesy, in his way, a different way perhaps, yet a telling way, recounted the run of his twenty-eight couple of hounds. He knew every foot of the ground, he knew the hounds and he even knew the fox. The run had lasted some two hours and three quarters, during which the line crossed and re-crossed the west road for the fox never made a longer point than four miles from the swamp. The judges apparently had many excellent opportunities from the roof of their automobile of scoring the hounds.

Mr. O'Shannesy was principally holding a brief for a hound whose gallantry and supreme fox hunting qualities had stirred his heart that day. Country people have great art in simple narrative for they live close to the things whereof they tell.

"General," he said, "that hound ran his fox like he was looking at him, looking at him every stride, and the fox a hundred rods afront of him. That hound don't think of anything only to catch the fox just as quick as he can catch him, and he don't wait, sir, to crawl under anything or poke his way through some cussed little place and get stuck and messed up. No sir, he takes 'em in his stride and keeps talking even when he's clear up in the air. I rode a ways up Hickory Lane and saw him come driving down off Hitchcliff Hill. He was like a stone, the farther he come the faster he was rolling.

"To look at him, General, maybe he wouldn't strike you as having much of a voice, but sir, his cry is like a piano, and he don't ever stop using it, not while there is a whiff of scent left. It seems like he could smell a fox clean over in the next county. He don't need scent strong enough to make a hound sneeze. No sir, he can drive along faster on a half scent than most hounds can run when they are looking at a fox, and he's talking to the line every foot of the way. I know you had a grand hound with you, General. I've known him since he was whelped, and his mother and father and back a long ways before that. He's a grand hound and I know it, but I wish you could have seen our hound run. I would have liked you to have seen him come off Hitchcliff Hill three hundred yards in front of the pack and running as straight a line as a man could draw on the ground. He didn't give that fox any chance to dwell or skylark about. Three times, General, I saw that hound in the same field with the fox and both of 'em digging their toes in the ground, and don't forget, General, that fox could go any place he had a mind to and run as fast as his legs could carry him, but all that hound had was just a mite of smell that he had to find and follow and stick to, and yet after two hours he was in the same field with the fox and pushing him. Gawd, General, how he pushed him."

At the end of his narrative Mr. O'Shannesy turned to Colonel Weatherford. "General Winkleford," he said, "Judge McCall and Mr. Monahan selected the winning hound and just before you came into the room we made the award because our folks were sort of wanting to get over to the dance and euchre party. As I said before, General, we are all mighty sorry the way the thing worked out but we sure appreciate you and Mr. Pinkleton coming such a long ways to judge for us, what with all the rain."

Mr. O'Shannesy sat down. I saw Colonel Weatherford

twice start to his feet, then apparently change his mind. Finally I heard his chair being pushed impetuously back and saw him rise to his feet. The hours of hard buffeting by the storm had caused his long but usually immaculately cared for mustache to droop in a manner which completely changed his facial expression. He looked for all the world like a ferocious grandfather walrus preparing to do battle. "Might I inquire," he asked in his iciest accent, "which hound won this hound trial and who owned the hound?" "Why, General," answered Mr. O'Shannesy, "it belongs to a kid, a sort of foreigner, who lives away back in the rocks. He's not here. He's only a little kid, but Gawd, General, he's got the runninest hound, the most no account lookin' white runt of a hound, but the runninest hound that ever crossed these hills."

CHAPTER X.

The Trevorts of Virginia Make Way

Following a meeting of the American branch of the International Society of Archeological Research, in Washington, Colonel Weatherford drifted down to Richmond to stay with some old friends.

Hearing that he had returned to Millbeck I dropped in on him to learn of this trip, and found him out under his elm tree deeply engrossed in a voluminous manuscript, some of the pages of which were frayed and yellow with age. He seemed moody and in low spirits and was obviously glad to see me, as though in need of diversion from whatever was engrossing him.

He told me of the meeting in Washington to discuss the Society's objectives for the next year, and of its recent achievements, but it was evident that his mind was on the manuscript. He gathered up the pages, held them in his hands and looked over at me, saying, "Pendleton, I suppose it is due to increasing years, but there are certain of the unalterable laws of nature which depress me. I resent the relentlessness with which things disintegrate, — families in particular.

"My friends in Richmond loaned me a series of journals, which they have succeeded in collecting, written by the elder branch of their family, to which they are only remotely connected. Pendleton, these early Virginians lived in magnificence. They were great sportsmen, royal hosts, and gallant gentlemen. What they did they did well. They imported the best stallions they could buy in England, the best cattle, the best of everything, and the colony prospered. These old journals give a more accurate, illuminating history of sport and life in the South than has ever been gathered between the covers of a book, but God bless my soul, Pendleton, it's impossible for me to enjoy them knowing that it all came to naught.

"I have marked a dozen or so entries by checks on the margin. Glance over them. It won't take you a moment. They illustrate what I mean, and form a saga of a great family. I rebel, Pendleton, at the withering up and ultimate effacement of families. Damn it if I don't detest changes of any kind."

The Colonel emptied his pipe by banging it viciously against the side of a bench, glared at me as though for fifteen cents he would reorganize this particular planet of ours preliminarily to turning his attention to the universe at large, — and took a turn of the garden.

The journals ran to some three hundred pages, written by different hands. The Colonel had inserted paper markers at the pages he wanted me to read.

THE TREVORTS OF VIRGINIA MAKE WAY.
From the Diary of Fairfax Churchill Trevort
1717 - 1778

MARCH 4TH, 1765. Dispatched my servant, Eff, to Richmond this day by mule-back to meet Lord Edgmont. Pray God the horse had a safe voyage from England.

My son, Fairfax Westmoreland Trevort born today.

MARCH 14TH, 1765. My horse, Lord Edgmont, for which I laid out the vast sum of a thousand pounds in England arrived safely this day and in good order. I do believe him to be the most airy and gallant-looking horse yet brought into this Colony. He unhappily savaged a blacksmith at Richmond.

MARCH 28TH, 1765. The gentlemen from all sections of this and neighboring parishes are kind enough to speak flatteringly about my stallion, Lord Edgmont, promising to send their most fashionable mares to him. The press does me the honor of prophesying that through this importation the horses in the entire Colony may be vastly improved.

SEPTEMBER 18TH, 1765. Dispatched Eff to Richmond to meet the ship bringing the silver for my daughter's wedding chest, 141 pieces in all, with the Trevort Arms. He is also to bring the items of finery my wife ordered from my agent in London. Eff took the covered wagon with four mules and three extra men as protection. The roads are in shocking condition for the entire 104 miles between this place and Richmond.

DECEMBER 31ST, 1765. As is my custom I will note at the year's close what measure of progress I have made in my affairs.

Through the acquisition of the Gwendollen lands Trevort Hall now embraces 14,600 acres of land by survey. There are 604 slaves on the place, an increase of 187 during the year. 400 additional acres of land have come under cultivation, five miles of new fences constructed, 184 cabins built, and an increase of live stock to the extent of some 300 head. My affairs are reaching a good state of order against, as my father was wont to say, the day when we must make way for others.

[159]

OCTOBER 10TH, 1770. This day ran my horse Edgmont of Trevort by Lord Edgmont a match race best 2 out of 3 heats for 500 pounds against Mr. Carroll St. Spencer's Hercules. Two more gallant horses never competed in this Colony.

I was privileged to entertain 150 or more of my neighbors following the event, many from a great distance.

I neglected to record that my horse was victorious. It was necessary for the horses to run the third heat, which was so near a draw that I found myself wishing it might have been so, more particularly as the match was run on the Trevort Downs. Feelings of cordiality engendered through being surrounded by one's friends in one's own halls are quite inimical to any pleasure from personal gain or success.

Eff had my horse in gratifying condition. He entertained the visiting attendants to the number of a hundred to a late hour. I am told there was much country dancing and that the singing was worthy.

NOVEMBER 3RD, 1770. Mr. Carroll St. Spencer this day challenged me to a main of 21 birds at 20 pounds the bird. I gladly accepted his challenge to give him an opportunity to recoup, but my cocks are not of the order I would wish. Will discuss the matter with Eff.

NOVEMBER 29TH, 1770. Was defeated in my main with Mr. St. Spencer and in so ignominious a manner that I must of necessity have lost caste with my neighbors. Only six of my twenty-one cocks were successful. I have written my agent in London to procure me some new stock of a breed of which I hear good report. The present deplorable situation comes from Eff's growing concern and interest in the horses and neglect of the cocks.

Eff's grandfather, old Eff, handled cocks for my grandfather with notable success, and one would think Eff would take a matter of such importance more seriously. I have promised him his freedom on Christmas day but in order to impress him with the gravity of not walking the birds sufficiently and permitting them to get into such low spirits, I told him I was of a mind to put the matter off for another year. This I will not do, but would certainly do to any other.

FAIRFAX WESTMORELAND TREVORT
1765 - 1840

MARCH 2ND, 1826. Eff went off to Richmond this day with a formidable cavalcade of men, mules and wagons to meet the ship from England bringing my new sire, Star Eclipse, the four blood mares and my new maroon coach which Messrs. Hooker built for me in London.

DECEMBER 31ST, 1826. As the year closes I note with satisfaction that my affairs have again prospered. The Trevort lands now extend to 19,000 acres, all properly surveyed, marked, and for the most part fenced with durable fencing. As my father used to say, — "Things are in good order against the time when we must make way for others."

FAIRFAX WESTMORELAND TREVORT II.
1803 - 1881

April 9th, 1865. The War ended today.

MARCH 3RD, 1870. I sent Eff over to Major Grosvenor's with my two old blood mares to have them bred. Were it not for false pride I would have the mares destroyed rather than send them to a horse of uncertain lineage — mares that trace back to Lord Edgmont and Star Eclipse. I seem not able, however, to reconcile myself to seeing a year pass without a foal or two at Trevort Hall. There is but one sire left in this part of the State.

My own affairs are desperate beyond all belief.

DECEMBER 31ST, 1870. I review the passing year with regret and dismay but thank God I face the future with courage and hope. Of the 19,000 acres once embracing this property, only 300 remain. The cattle barns, stables and sheep folds are empty and standing with the air of expecting further devastation; weeds and neglect reproach me when I walk abroad.

I purpose nevertheless by the strictest possible economy, by eternal vigilance, and by my own continual labors, with the help of Almighty God to restore again our fortunes, against, as my father used to say, the time when we must make way for others.

While reviewing the year I would record one pleasant event, our marriage anniversary, at which above a hundred of our valued friends partook of our modest hospitality. Many of them did us the kindness of staying on with us for a week or more. Some were put to burdensome expense in coming so great a distance. Since the war most of our friends have dispensed with their coaches and did us honor to ride such wearisome journeys. My memory glows at the remembrance of the many kindly and courteous sentiments which were expressed for us.

As I am writing this entry Mr. Spencer called upon me challenging me to a main of six birds at two dollars the bird. I accommodated him. I will impress upon Eff that I want our birds very painstakingly walked, and will see to the business myself.

FRANCIS FAIRFAX CHURCHILL TREVORT
1845 - 1927

FEBRUARY 3RD, 1887. This day the Planters Security and Trust Co. took over Trevort Hall under the mortgage. Mr. Phillips, the young man in charge of the company's affairs very courteously offered to permit us the temporary use and occupancy of the superintendent's cottage. I am most grateful to him. I must now promptly engage in some enterprise which will insure my affairs being in better order when the time comes for me to make way in favor of my son.

DECEMBER 23RD, 1923. Mr. Bob Jordan has this day invited me to join with him in his merchandising enterprise at Spillman Cross Roads. His exacting duties as Postmaster, to which post he has just been appointed, precludes his giving the necessary attention to his place of business.

Mr. Jordan very generously contracts to pay me the emolument of eight dollars per week and the use of the two rooms over the store, the one for me, the other for Eff, and consents to my paying Eff the sum of two dollars per week to help me in lifting the heavier articles. I am grateful for being able to make this satisfactory arrangement regarding Eff. His family, father, and son, have been attached to my family for some five generations. His loyalty to me in certain rather perplexing situations has touched me deeply.

DECEMBER 23RD, 1925. I am 80 years of age today, and Eff is now 81.

NOVEMBER 3RD, 1927. I was not able to wait upon our patrons today due to a slight but now continuing indisposition. The thought has occurred to me many times lately that the day is not far off when I must make way for others. I think constantly of my son, Francis. How could he let so many years go by, eighteen years it is now, without letting me know his whereabouts?

FRANCIS CHURCHILL TREVORT
1878 - 1928

From the Richmond *Dispatch* of December 14th, 1928:

"Francis C. Trevort formerly of this State died at the South Chicago Poor Farm, December 13th. He had been an inmate of the institution for some years."

CHAPTER XI.

Pamela Weatherford

I N that now remote era when an older generation was expected to gasp at the lack of manners, convention and propriety of youth, the one intimate contact which old Colonel Weatherford had with what he called "this social disorder," was furnished by his niece, Pamela Weatherford, of Boston.

If, for educational reasons, the Colonel had to be initiated into this then considered disturbing new order of things, certainly he could have found no more modern example to study than this same niece of his. The difficulty was that he made not the slightest effort to comprehend her and had no intention of trying to do so.

The Colonel was brusque, critical, and at times almost belligerent with his youthful kinswoman. He stormed at her when present and about her when absent, threatening her with every form of chastisement, from things physical to deleting her name from his will.

Pamela listened to these scoldings and protests with only an academic interest in what she referred to as "Uncle John's deliciously whimsical Victorianisms," and went on her way believing and announcing to all who cared to listen that she was possessed of the most lovable, engaging, prehistoric uncle in the world.

But the odd and difficult thing to understand about all this furore, scolding and indignation was that underneath it the old Colonel was inordinately proud of his niece, and as a matter of fact very much in love with her. On the other hand he couldn't and wouldn't countenance many things. He disliked her matter of fact way of indulging when thirsty in a whiskey and soda. In the Colonel's scheme of things neither young girls nor old girls consumed whiskey and soda. He stormed at her approval of certain books. He berated her for wagering more than she could afford to risk at Belmont and Saratoga. Never partaking of and seldom serving cocktails, which he considered as so much poison, it irritated him beyond measure to hear Pamela requisition a cocktail from his own butler and then to ask for the dividend.

Her sailing for odd, unconventional parts of Europe on a day's notice, junketing about the world alone and dropping out of sight for long periods of time, he considered gross irregularities.

If she failed to come to see him he felt abused and lonesome, yet when advised that she was coming he felt even more abused, for one of the continuing causes of rupture between them lay in Pamela's haphazard way of pouncing upon him at untoward times and making requests tending to upset his well-ordered life and household. One of the Colonel's chief complaints was of her arriving at any hour between midnight and sun-up, with one or more attachés, after every Yale-Harvard football game played in New Haven, and wheedling him out of a horse to hunt on Monday. The entire situation was ridiculous but perhaps not altogether unnatural, for the Colonel was too old to have a niece of Pamela's years, and particularly at a time when girls were making their first use of a freedom totally incomprehensible to him.

The Colonel was stubborn and set and old-fashioned, focusing upon his niece's lesser characteristics and refusing to see the mountains or give credit where credit was due. Comparatively speaking Pamela was not much beyond a child, yet had made a distinguished mark for herself. She had translated a volume of very difficult modern French verse for an exacting publisher, and with so much charm and feeling that the American edition had sold far beyond the publisher's expectation.

A famous collector, the owner of a rare and ancient manuscript, having twice failed to procure a satisfactory translation, turned the text over to her; and some day there will be a new and very important book on sport.

She had an intuitive appreciation of the subtle meanings and appropriateness of words, the new and happy use of which made her tingle with glee. The scheme of things which she had mapped out for herself called for her being up to the minute in things literary, in the arts and in the important movements of the day, and being wound up to a high key she readily absorbed current happenings.

Nature had been most extraordinarily bountiful with her and this, augmented by a munificent allowance plus her own knowledge of countless subtle artifices, made of her a picture that caused the old Colonel to mutter to me more than once, "God bless me, Pendleton." Following these "God bless me's" he would indulge in a certain amount of scolding and berating regarding cocktails and betting and then carry her off for a day's racing at Belmont Park or Saratoga, wagering a hundred dollars of his own money on every race or two for her, a thing which he never did for himself, then order an artistically conceived dinner and the best of wine and take inordinate pride in introducing her as "my niece" to any old acquaintance within view.

But whatever she turned her hand to seemed to irritate the Colonel. She did a sketch for Hollywood that brought a reward which when I reduced it to terms of my black Angus beef at nine cents a pound, astounded me and suggested the futility of agriculture as a livelihood. The Colonel read the manuscript and no one lacking his iron constitution could have carried on as he did without suffering a stroke. I myself had to squirm a bit at the flaunting of things I thought it unnecessary to parade. That the name Weatherford was to be subscribed to the piece shook the Colonel to his foundations.

Following this she became entranced with Russian dancing, fell under the spell of a group of Russian exiles in Montreal, wore herself to a shadow mastering the technique, and, favored with beauty, charm and a figure given to few dancers, blossomed out under a Russian name. She took unto herself an alleged Russian prince as a partner and gave recitals. Just how the Colonel survived this storm, terrific in its intensity, I don't know.

All things considered, I knew Pamela Weatherford a great deal better than did her uncle, and a sounder, saner, clearer-thinking, straighter-shooting little person never lived. John Weatherford represented her ideal of a gentleman, and a man of the world and a sportsman of the older generation, but she was just as much a Weatherford as he was and could be just as set in her ways. She was determined to live her own life and see it through along her own lines.

It was shortly after the Russian dancing phase and when

the Colonel was about able to refer to her again without exploding, that he received a letter at the reading of which I happened to be present.

"Darling," she commenced. I could never be sure whether this mode of address irritated or pleased him. "I want awfully to go to Virginia to hunt. I have never been there. And listen, darling, my boy is the most terrible rotter. Couldn't I have your Eddie Walsh and your van and couldn't he come up to Boston for my horses and van them down to Centerburg? Couldn't you possibly come with me? I'm going to Rome as soon as I get back, and won't see you for ever so long. Please dear, come down with me — just for ten days. I have worlds of things I want to talk to you about and ask you about. I've been terribly good lately. Is it all right about the van? Can I stay two or three days with you before I sail? God keep you and make you love me a little bit because I love you — and keep you from being so terribly cross with me.

Pam."

I could tell perfectly well from the manner in which the note paper crinkled in the Colonel's hand that we were in for an explosion. He sat holding the letter, looking into the fire and tapping his foot on the floor while I waited in unhappy expectancy, confessing to myself that I would relish a fortnight hunting in Virginia with Pamela Weatherford. I marvelled at that rugged old New England conservatism which permitted a man to act like a bear to anyone so completely beguiling.

The Colonel prolonged his meditation, apparently forgetful of my very existence, a welcome neglect. I knew what was in progress. He was framing one of those crisp telegrams which would commence with the statement that he could not spare Walsh and the van, and then enlarge upon the unwarranted expense and impropriety of going to Rome, and include a reference to an affair of some years ago which caused the Colonel to make a quick trip to Rome, to bring her home, the inconvenience and annoyance of which rankled him to this day. He suddenly shoved his chair back, arose, and started, as I supposed, to the telephone; I resigned myself to being an ear witness to the sending of a very pompous telegram, and so slumped down in my chair. But instead of essaying the telephone the Colonel rang a bell and instructed the servant to send Walsh to him. The very tone of his voice assured me that the storm had passed.

When Eddie Walsh arrived, a servant who from boyhood had caused the Colonel quite as much mental annoyance as his niece, the Colonel said to him, "Walsh, have Eugène go over the van thoroughly in the morning and make sure that it is in good order, then go to Boston and pick up Miss Weatherford's horses and take them to Centerburg, Virginia, to Mr. Furrman's stables. You will be away about ten days. Take our own head-stalls and clothes. I won't have horses unloaded from my van with rags on them. Here is two hundred dollars. You will pay your own expenses and Mr. Furrman's bill. I don't want Miss Weatherford to pay any of the bills, and Walsh, I want you to report to me how everything goes. Now don't forget that. Report everything. I will write out directions in the morning showing you how to reach Centerburg. That is all." The boy was starting to leave the room when the Colonel called him back. "Walsh," he said, "I want you to understand that you are working for Miss Weatherford. Now don't forget. I don't want anyone in Virginia to think I own those old crocks of horses or ever had anything to do with them or even saw them or that they ever saw Millbeck. Remember, they are Miss Weatherford's horses and come from Boston. You needn't go out of your way even to mention that Miss Weatherford is my niece, and don't take any clothing with my initials on it, and don't leave the van out on the public square."

When the boy had left the room the Colonel re-read the letter, folded it, took it over and placed it in a bulky envelope, retied a piece of red tape around the envelope and placed it in the lower drawer of his desk. "Pendleton," he said, "I'm now going to give you a supreme licking at backgammon." As we started to play he put the dice down, and looked at me saying, "I would give pretty nearly anything I have in this world if she would just marry the right sort of man. And if I had anything left after I had given everything away I would give it as a thank-offering if I could cease being so fond of her."

Something over a week went by when one afternoon the Colonel telephoned asking if he could stroll over and see me. He seemed in rather a contemplative yet slightly perplexed frame of mind, a mood I enjoyed, for at such times he was judicial and infinitely human.

"Pendleton," he commenced, "I rather think I should run down to Virginia. Do you think you could steal off for a few days. We could stop over and see the Pimlico Futurity and I would rather like to see that race this year. A colt of my breeding is starting. The truth is, Pamela is a bit on my mind. I rather gather that — well here Pendleton, perhaps you would glance over these letters which that jackass Walsh has written me. I'm sorry to bother you with so much rubbish but you couldn't appraise the situation without reading the letters, and I want your advice." The Colonel handed me the letters, told my man to bring him a glass of sherry and a biscuit, took a book over to a favorite leather arm chair, while I settled down to read Eddie Walsh's reports.

Centerburg, Virginia.

Hon. Colonel John Weatherford
    Millbeck, New York
    Sir:

I got your letter saying as how I was to report the way everything went down here with Miss Pamela and me and the horses.

Well, Sir, I wouldn't know how to report the kind of a place this Centerburg, Virginia, is, it not being like any other place I ever been in not by no manner of means.

We got here pretty good with the van, only account of me loosing the paper you gave me, I went to a place called West Virginia, what is only a spell one side of where I was going then I found the paper and got here.

Now please, Sir, I wouldn't want to say anything I shouldn't only these two horses of Miss Pamela's well Sir, they arn't the kind of horses you'd be after thinking a young lady would be buying if there were any other two horses any wheres. Not at all at all. The black horse is called Lord Ronald. A man wouldn't know how to get four pounds for him in Cork as a carter. The dun mare, Kiss Me, is worser than him by a pound. When we was unloading, Mr. Furrman, where I'm stabling, said to me, "Have you got papers for these horses?" And a colored boy what works for him acted like he would choke. I didn't say nothing to the boy, not then.

[172]

I will report more tomorrow. Everything is all right only I don't know how as I will get along so good with this Lord Ronald and this Kiss Me whats the orfulest looking mare.

Respectfully,

Eddie.

Centerburg, Virginia

Hon. Colonel John Weatherford
  Millbeck, New York
Sir:

Miss Pamela came to the stable this morning and said as how she wanted to hunt in the morning and would ride Lord Ronald and I was to ride Kiss Me, and she said the people down here when they rode blood horses did their horses manes up in little kind of curlpaper knots and wanted her horses done the same way, and had I ever seen curlpaper knots and could I learn to do it. Now please, Sir, Miss Pamela asking me could I braid a horse's mane and me braidin' 'em for you three days a week these fifteen years. But the dun mare has had her mane hogged for maybe twenty years and is just growing a mane and the hairs are terrible bristly, and she's got too many of 'em, and you can't thin 'em — and her mane is black, and when I get through she's goin' to have maybe a million braids what's goin' to stick out 'stead of bein' flat, and be the orfulest lookin' horse. Then Miss Pamela said she saw horses going to the Meet with sort of football guards on their knees and the lead horses with sheets that fitted over their ears —sort of window curtain material, and did I have any of these football things and lace curtains, and if not I was to get them at the saddle shop.

Well, Sir, please, I thought that would be all but Miss Pa-

[173]

mela says as how she went with a young gentleman what lives at the same place as her, to see the horses training at Mr. Heigler's track and that the young gentleman told her that they were going to have a hunter trial down here next week, and then she told me she had decided to enter Lord Ronald and wanted him put in training. Please, Sir, that's what Miss Pamela said, "put him in training." If you will excuse me, Sir, it's the most ridiculest thing ever I heard. But I have something worser than that to report. Miss Pamela wants to know can I ride with my stirrups pulled up short like a jockey and have I any blinkers in the tack box and is there one of these walking canes what you can sit on in the tack box and did I bring any field glasses, 'cause she wants to go out early in the morning and sit on the walking cane and watch me through the glasses breezing Lord Ronald and will I please do him up in bandages all around and pull my stirrups just as short as Mr. Heigler's boys 'cause if she is going to put Lord Ronald in training she is going to do it correct.

Please, Sir, I don't want to give any offense but I was thinking was I to report this why maybe you might telegraph Miss Pamela 'cause me galloping Lord Ronald 'round Mr. Heigler's track 'long side of his good race horses, me with my stirrups pulled way up, Lord Ronald wearing blinkers and all bandaged up and Miss Pamela sitting on one of these here little canes and lookin' at me is the turbelest, orfulest things what ever was at any time.

I'm 'most through reporting only this afternoon just when I was leaving the stable Admiral Payson, the first part is about the sea and all that, but the sea isn't right here at Centerburg, only the Admiral has a fine farm and breeds only race horses and has the grandest stallion altogether what can't be used only to thoroughbred mares. Well it seems him and Miss Pamela was having some supper together at his house last night and he says to me, "Are you Miss Weatherford's man?" "Yes sir," I says. "Well, show me Miss Weatherford's mare — the one she wants to breed to my horse. I never accept any mares without inspecting them. Have you a proper health certificate for her? How recently has she been examined?" Well, Sir, please I take him down to the dun mare's box. "No. No," he says, "I only want to see the mare she wants to breed. I have no time to look over all her horses." "Well, Sir," I says, "this is the only mare we have down here." "What?" he says, "What? What?" and goes in the box. "God," he says. "Good Lord," and turns to a gentleman what's with him and the gentleman says, "Lord a-Mighty," and they both say Lord a-Mighty a couple of more times, then go away.

This is all what I have to report now, Sir.

Respectfully,

Eddie.

Centerburg, Virginia

Hon. Colonel John Weatherford
Millbeck, New York
Sir:

This was the day we hunted. Please, Sir, it don't seem like I know where to start.

Well I did all those things Miss Pamela wanted, knee pads and such, and the boys in the stable standing around watching me and there were some more boys from outside standing around and one of the boys who didn't get there 'till after I had the net on Lord Ronald says to a boy in the stable. "What horse is that?" and the boy says, "Why that's Colonel

[175]

Bradley's Kentucky Derby winner." I didn't say anything. Not right then.

The Meet was seven miles away over the turbelest road and I never saw so many horses on a road in my life. There was more people to the Meet than would be in Millbeck in a year.

Everybody here in Virginia is mostly interested in horses. They don't pay attention any to people, only it be someone what looks like Miss Pamela, but you wouldn't have a horse out of a van long enough to pull a tail bandage off afore they would know all about him.

Well, Sir, seeing me coming along with Lord Ronald all done up, what with lace curtains and all, why they kept lookin' at him and I see by the way they looked at his feet and legs and the face of him, they can't make nothing of it all at all 'cause please Sir no one ever saw legs like of his on a hunter. You wouldn't know that a horse could find the time or enough places to put the bumps and old cuts on his legs as this Lord Ronald has. And his feet, why please Sir you wouldn't see none of a napkin if one of 'em was standing on it. An English groom from Philadelphia says to me, "that 'orse must have been in some 'orrible haccidents."

Well I didn't see any other horses done up like I had my horses, and then I knowed Miss Pamela had seen some flat horses being taken over to Mr. Heigler's track and that's where she got the idea about this net and all.

I didn't want to take the sheet off and the knee pads and tail bandages and all what with every one lookin' at me, but there didn't seem any use of waiting, so took 'em off, and I haven't the sheet more than off when a boy who works for some people from Boston says, "God if it ain't old Lord Ron-

ald come down here for his 21st birthday." But Sir a meet is
no place, not by no manner of means, to say anything or do
anything to anybody but afore I leave I got something to say
to this Boston boy and the one what said Lord Ronald was
Colonel Bradley's Kentucky Derby winner and the one what
laughed when Mr. Furrman asked me did I have the papers
and three others what I didn't report about but were worser
than any.

Miss Pamela came along then with three young gentlemen,
I think it was five she come along with, and I put her up and
she says, "Walsh, is Lord Ronald all right? He isn't nervous
or upset about being in a strange stable or off his feed, is he,
Walsh?" Please Sir, you haven't seen this Lord Ronald and
him bein' nervous and upset is the rediculist thing.

Well, hounds moved off up the road a spell, to a wood,
but we didn't go in the covert but kept on till we come to a
bar way what a boy let down and we went across a field to a
hill and stood on the hill. I never saw so many horses to a
Meet and a lot o 'em young and just bein' schooled and I
never saw three-year-olds so nice and quiet and the boys sit-
tin' on 'em quiet and it's the same in the stables down here,
everything quiet, and the stables don't look like nothing at
all on the outside but all clean and neat on the inside and the
tack nice and soft; and like I said nobody makin' any noise,
no droppin' things and hollerin' at a colt to move over and
all this. I never saw many of these colored boys before and
you wouldn't think I was reporting what was the truth but
please, Sir, some of these boys ride and handle a young horse
almost like maybe they had been in Ireland.

An Irish boy whose people live on Long Island says to me,
"Where do you get your horses?" looking impertinent like at

Kiss Me. "Melton Mowbray," I says, and I'm going to do the same by him as those other boys I reported about.

I ain't told you about this Kiss Me. I don't know how Lord Ronald feels under you but this Kiss Me is the turbelest feelin' horse ever I rode. She's got feet bigger than the black horse and puts 'em down flat and leaves 'em there like she was counting or tryin' to remember which one was down afore she would pull it up.

We stood on the hill maybe ten minutes everybody lookin' at everybody else's horse when of a sudden hounds found and went out the far end of the covert. The Master they have down here does good by the hounds. When hounds go away he don't move, don't pay any attention to 'em only to know what way they are goin'. He just keeps on talking. He waits till he figures the fox means to run and when he starts you got enough to do to keep hounds in sight without gallopin' in front of the fox or stamping on hounds tails and scarin' 'em. So pretty soon the Master moves off, walkin', then joggin', then canterin' slow, and first thing we are steppin' along over some fields that don't look like they had any start or end to 'em.

Well, Sir, please, I figures I was to keep an eye on Miss Pamela as good as I could so I kicked this Kiss Me along as smart as she had a mind to move which ain't anything at all, me trying to keep as close up front as a groom would feel like being and I see Miss Pamela clean up 'long side the Master, and that old Lord Ronald pounding away, his head down 'tween his knees and I see by the way Miss Pamela is riding, givin' and takin' at the reins and tryin' to snatch his head up, that the horse is no gentleman and she not bein' able to hold him, not by no manner of means.

[178]

'Course I'm worried about Miss Pamela but please Sir it was myself had some troubles too. The leps were all kinds, chicken coops, stone walls, bar-ways, and some of the tur-belest dry ditches ever I seen and I'm not telling any thing but the truth when I report Sir that this Kiss Me hit every jump in that whole part of Virginia, and please, Sir, she don't just tick 'em — not like an old brush horse that ticks 'em all, front and back, 'cause he feels more comfortable like when he feels em, no Sir, she just bangs right into 'em, but it don't seem to bother her none. She don't peck or act like she even knew she hit 'em.

A gentleman rode up 'long side of me after she hit a coop so hard she carries it with her maybe half a rod, and says, "That mare must have calooses, calooses all up and down her legs." I didn't know what these calooses were so I just says, "Yes sir, thank you."

You see, Sir, these coops, in wire fences, have the wire un-derneath 'em. They don't cut the wire but only bend it down and build the coop over it. Well, Sir, please, they anchor these coops down pretty tight to the ground 'cause there don't be anything more turrible than to hit a jump and have the jump go along with you all messed up under your horse 'cause you can't even fall and get it over with or anything. You just keep fallin' only nothin' happens 'till you come to the end of how far the wire will stretch, then you fall so fast you don't get any chance to get free. I never saw any horse only this Kiss Me hit a coop hard enough to take it along, and when it wouldn't go any further and it kind a ridin' along under her belly she give a mite of a lurch and maybe grunt and gets her legs free and away we'd go. Please, Sir, there don't be any sense, not by no manner of means, of a horse going to all this trouble and worrying a rider instead of jump-in' over the top. Twice when she did this the wire made a noise — kind of a singing noise, and Mr. Furrman what was near me, says, "Walsh, either go on with the mare or ride her back of me 'cause I don't lay to jump any more of these coops while they're dancin' about and screamin'."

But what she did to the coops was nothin' like what she did to these stone walls. The stones on these walls arn't bigger than what a man could carry in a 4 quart measure — not like those walls up to New England, and when the mare sees what they're like seems as though she 'most laughs at 'em and starts droppin' her hind legs, and please, Sir, you wouldn't know the noise these little stones make, and herself pulling some of 'em 5 rods out into the fields and pretty soon I have maybe 20 colored boys on three-year-olds following me through the gaps I'm after making and once I looked back and here's a boy on a shetland pony what joined the hunt when we went through a farm and the pony is walking through the gap. Please, Sir, don't that be the orfulest thing, me, what's always riddin' your grand horses, carrying on this a way in a hunt?

I'm thinking maybe the mare's legs must be all cut and asks Mr. Furrman would he tell me and he says she don't have a scratch, and please Sir, don't that be the wonderfullest thing how she can go plowin' right through those walls, some of 'em four feet, groaning and grunting the way she does, tear-ing down maybe five feet of the beautifulest wall and not get a scratch? And maybe you wouldn't know Sir that having all them millions of little short, black braids sticking out like they done and her being such a light dun color and havin' such a plain head, why people kept lookin' at me more than usual.

'Course I knew the Hunt wouldn't like this way of lepping and like I knew, the man who rides in the back to see that the gates are closed and all, comes up to me and asks whose horse it is and I tell him and he writes it down and says to me, "Did you school that mare? Did you make her for the lady?" and I says no. "Well," he says, "could you show me the man who did school her?" and I says I don't know where she came from but I thought she came from Virginia. "Ireland," he says. "Virginia," I says. "Ireland," he says. But please, Sir, you wouldn't be interested in all what happened.

I didn't mean to report so much about this mare and forget the hunt. Well, we'd run that fox maybe 35 minutes and I do pretty good what with cutting corners in keeping hounds and Miss Pamela in view when all at oncet we come bang up to what they call down here the Haywood land. Please, Sir, you wouldn't understand what I'm going to report unless I tell you about this land. It seems, Sir, that a long time ago one of these Haywoods had trouble with the Hunt and since then the Hunt can't go across that land — 2000 acres it is, and the ridenest, foxyest looking land ever I see in the world, and here we was, hounds a flying on and no one can get to 'em even to blow 'em off, and all the ladies and gentlemen standing there.

Well, whatever took hold of that Lord Ronald a person wouldn't know. He's standing quiet like, 'long side of the Master and I'm starting to ride up to Miss Pamela to see if her tack is all right and everything, when if that black horse what's been looking to where hounds went and acting a mite restless don't give kind of a lunge and snatch at his head, wicked like, and afore I know what's goin' on he pops the fence what we were standing 'long side of and he's no

[181]

sooner over than he starts lugging and snatching at the bit,
and Miss Pamela doing all she can to get his head up and
stop him or turn him but she can't stop him, and the Master
standing up in his stirrups, calling, "hold hard, hold hard,"
and everybody calling, "hold hard," and there being no one
holding as hard as Miss Pamela. Well I'm standin' there
and the Master 'count of seeing me come to the meet with
the two horses says, "go and stop her. That land's closed.
She's apt to get shot. There is no excuse for her going on
that way."

Well, Sir, please, I hop over the fence but in the first
place this mare has no foot and in the second place, Sir, a
man wouldn't find such a galloping country, not any place,
and worser still hounds are only in the next field and running beautiful, Sir. And in the next place to that why, why,
well Sir, please, afore I report it, would your honor please
not mention it? You see Sir, I wasn't so sure, not as sure as
a person should be, that Lord Ronald was going away with
Miss Pamela. You see, Sir, I thought maybe Miss Pamela
hadn't tried as hard as she could to stop the horse. Well, I
make a great flourish to catch up — I'm booting the mare
and slaps her over the quarter with my hand and carryin'
on and all that 'till first thing I knew we are out of sight
of the field. Well, Sir, if I had been on a good horse I
guess maybe I would have had the finest hunt ever a man
had. It's that country I'd like your honor to see. There don't
be a farm in Millbeck like it at all at all. Not a stone, not a
woodchuck hole, not a weed higher than a pansy, just miles
of grand country, and Miss Pamela and me and the hounds
and a scent a hound could smell in the next county.

Well I got to come to the bad part now. We are galloping

up a nice pasture field when I see a man running towards us. He has a dog with him and been shooting. Well, he stands right in our way, and Sir, when we get close to him he up and shoots off his gun — not shootin' at us but over our heads, and he shoots a second time and Miss Pamela starts to turn her horse and gallop past him but I hollers to her to stop 'cause how did I know whether the man was maybe drunk or crazy, so she stopped and the man walked right up to her and takes hold of her bridle. I never see a man so mad — turrible mad he was, Sir. He were young, and a gentleman, and if I do say it Sir, as grand a lookin' young gentleman as ever I see, but so mad I think maybe he is crazy, and I'm wishin' I had Miss Pamela safe out on the road again.

Well, Sir, he starts to talk, but Miss Pamela she didn't let him. Do you remember Sir me tellin' you that the young gentleman was mad. Well, maybe I thought he was mad, but please, Sir, he didn't know how to get mad at all at all, not by no manner of means. He didn't have no idea of how to get mad. Why, Miss Pamela was so much madder than him that he didn't act like he was mad at all. Why, Sir, please, I never knew not by no manner of means how a young lady could get mad, nor what they can do when they are mad. Perhaps, Sir, you wouldn't see how it was, but he was standing there with his gun and we were trespassing, and maybe he was crazy.

Well, first place she tells him to let go of her horse, and she don't ask him but once. He let go it like it burned his fingers. Then she tells him what she thinks of a make-be-lieve man — that's what she called him —that would shoot his gun off at a woman. And she says if he lived up in her

[183]

country the first gentleman he met would give him a hid-
ing that would do him good. Then she tells him she don't
want to hear that the land is closed 'cause she knows all
about it.

But, Sir, even if I wanted to report to you all what she
said I couldn't do it. She talked turrible fast and there were
never any gentlemen, not any gentlemen who ever lived,
heard so much about themselves and their fathers and them
that come before that. But, Sir, there is one thing I got to
say about that Mr. Haywood. Just as soon as Miss Pamela
started to talk he got over his mad, clear over it. He acted
like he couldn't take his eye off her, and it seemed to me he
was smilin' and liked listening to her and wanted her to go
on tellin' him what she thought of him and his folks, or
anything else she'd have a mind to talk about.

'Course, Sir, please, if you don't mind me sayin' so, you
wouldn't see a lady like Miss Pamela once maybe in a life-
time. Why, people were talkin' about her at the Meet and
askin' who she was and all. There don't be many people
what hunt looks like she looks. Well, when she finishes
tellin' him those things she says, "Mr. Haywood, my man
and I are going to hunt this fox until we kill him, put him
to earth or loose him, and if you have anything better than
sawdust under your jacket, which I don't believe you have,
you'll get on a horse and come with us, or better still, get on
my second horse." She turns to me and says, "Give Mr.
Haywood the mare."

Well, Sir he didn't say a word, just slipped up on the
mare, gave her a kick in the ribs and let his stirrups down as
he rode, and first thing I knew I was standin' there alone
holdin' his gun and not knowin' where I was or where to go.

There was a nice piece of a hill 'long side of me so I stepped to the top and had a fine view of the farm, and was just thinkin', if you'll excuse me, Sir, what a grand gallop you and Miss Mary and Mr. Pendleton could be after havin' across that land, when I see some cattle running 'way off north. Then I see the hounds.

Well, Sir, I stayed up on that hill 'most an hour and see hounds maybe ten times and Miss Pamela and that Mr. Haywood well up with them 'count of him knowin' the land so good, 'cause that mare couldn't have kept up only by him cuttin' corners like that. He were a fine horseman, Sir, and there weren't ever a better runnin' fox in the world, nor a grander country, Sir, to run him in, and them two havin' it to themselves, and it was a grand afternoon. Then the fox seemed like he headed away north, so I walked a couple of miles to where I saw some buildings, and it's the house, so I find the stable and tells the boy what's going on, only he don't believe me, so I just sit down to wait, only I don't feel so good 'count of leavin' Miss Pamela alone that a way, but please, Sir, there was nothing I could do when she orders me to get off the mare and give her to Mr. Haywood. There don't be any use of me tryin' to run after the hounds afoot, not in that kind of a country.

Well, Sir, it's pretty near dark when I hear horses comin' shufflin' down the lane and they have the hounds with them, and there is the end of a brush stickin' out of Miss Pamela's pocket.

The colored boy and me got the hounds put away in two box stalls, then I take the horses, not knowin' what's goin' to happen next.

Miss Pamela and Mr. Haywood go off a little way and

[185]

start talkin'. Now, please, Sir, I don't say this like I was complaining, but only to report to you how it all was, but they stood talkin' a whole half hour, and Miss Pamela she wasn't mad that time, the two of them looking at each other and looking. Bye and bye Mr. Haywood comes over to me and says, "I will motor Miss Weatherford back to town after tea. You go along with the horses. I will phone for the hound van, and he gave me five dollars and asks me what I did with his gun, then he and Miss Pamela goes up to the house.

This is all I got to report, Sir.

Respectfully,

Eddie.

P. S.

Please, Sir, I am down at the post office to mail this letter. I saw the Master at the corner talking to another gentleman and we were waiting for some cars to go by and I heard the Master say to the other gentleman, "The Haywood land has been opened to the Hunt after 40 years."

P. S. again.

Please, Sir, Miss Pamela just come in here to the post office for her mail and says to me, "Eddie, I'm moving up to stay with Mr. Haywood and his mother. Take the horses and tack up there this afternoon," and then she said, "Eddie, I may stay down in Virginia longer than I thought — in fact," she says, "I might stay quite a long time — a very long time, so I think you had better arrange to take Colonel Weatherford's van back to Millbeck. Mr. Haywood's boy can do my horses. I will write Colonel Weatherford."

So now, please, Sir, what am I to do? It seems like I better start home the way it looks.

[186]

Please, Sir, another P. S.

When Miss Pamela got out on the street she came back into the post office just when I was buying a stamp, and says, "Eddie, don't you ever tell anybody down here that you saw me kick Lord Ronald into that fence, and Eddie," she says, "it may be that when the old horse passes on I will put that little bit of him where my heel rubbed into a locket."

Please, Sir, a body wouldn't know what a young lady like Miss Pamela would be after doing or saying next, not by no manner of means.

Eddie.

CHAPTER XII.

The Return of "Riley"

THE 1926 Hound Show at the Riding Club in New York was in full swing. Judges of English hounds, American hounds, halfbred hounds, harriers and beagles had been hard at work since early morning. There were beagles over thirteen inches, and beagles under thirteen inches, classes for hound dogs whelped since January 1, 1924, and bitch hounds whelped at any time, pack classes and classes for couples of any sex, and monetary awards to Huntsmen for the bloom and manners of their charges.

The closing gong having sounded on the floor of the Stock Exchange, lovers of horse and hound from the financial district were soon pressing into the tanbark arena. Someone said, "They will judge the class for the Championship American Dog Hound in a minute." Instinctively we crowded about the ring. Even devotees of the English hound could not resist having a look, a conservative, restrained, doubting look.

An official announced, "Class for the Best American Dog Hound, — in the ring, please." The competition was on. There were blue ticked hounds from the "Eastern Shore" — long-eared, deep-throated hounds from Pennsylvania — small, active, red hounds with finely chiseled heads from up and down the Rappahannock River in Virginia, and hounds from Kentucky whose owners talked of July or Walker blood. The Judge went to work. The same official consulted a card and said, "There is one more entry." The M. F. H. of the Fairfield and Westchester hounds entered the ring with Riley.

When on the following morning fox hunters from far and near turned to the sporting pages of the *Times* and the *Tribune* they read, "Fairfield and Westchester Hounds' Riley adjudged the best American Dog Hound at the Annual Hound Show." Later Riley swept the boards at Bryn Mawr, winning the Championship and Medal of the National Fox Hounds Association.

Someone said it would be educational to construct a composite picture from likenesses of different American hounds representing different types, particularly in view of the oft-heard reproval that there is no true type of American fox hound. It was done, and the effort produced an interesting effigy of an American fox hound bitch.

They started on the American dog hound. The Committee faltered before a likeness of Riley. Could they after all improve on the thing they already had in this picture, by trying to embody this or that? They thought not, and so the picture depicting the Committee's best judgment of a true type of an American fox hound stands today the literal photograph of Riley.

From then on that magnificent Walker hound was photographed, painted, and talked about as only prima donnas are talked about. Following his triumph he returned to kennels, was drafted when his days to be drafted came around, and

"The melody of eager, pressing voices filled the valley."

hunted his fox up and down the Mianus Valley during the winter.

Then came a day when hounds met at the Round Hill Store, an old time fixture. It was Thanksgiving, the premier holiday of all the year for fox hunters. Riley, as becoming a champion, had been drafted. We drew north and drifted along to the Quaker Ridge covert. There hounds found and went away on a stiff-necked fox.

Through all the decades of fox hunting much good song and verse has been written on Thanksgiving Day runs, and those who were of the first flight at Greenwich on Thanksgiving Day, 1926, had material for many a verse. That stalwart pack of hounds hunted, and drove, and drove and hunted that good-running fox north, south, east and west. He must have been an old timer who ran for the love of the sport. Time after time he passed hospitable and safe "earths" but still ran on.

With the pack running strong and pressing him he headed away to make his point. As hounds raced across the grasslands just below the Agnew meadows we had a good view of them. There, out in front, leading the pack, was Riley. The M. F. H. was heard to say, "It's Riley's fox. He found him. He has stuck to that line every foot of the way. That's the sort of drive that kills foxes."

Then, as ever happens in woodland hunting, the line entered an extensive covert. The melody of eager, pressing voices filled the valley. A shot rang out. "Some gunners about" was what we said, and thrust forward to hounds.

Later, very much later, that day, hounds accounted for their fox on the fringes of Rye Lake. In the fading light of late afternoon the Master blew his hounds to him preparatory to the long jog home. One by one hounds came to the horn. To the casual observer they might have all seemed accounted for, and yet the horn twanged and twanged across the darkening hills. The "field" drifted home to tea, but the horn blew on. One who ever liked to hack home with hounds said to the Master, "How long before you start?" "I don't know," was the reply. "He hasn't come in yet." "Who — one of the whippers-in?" "No, Riley." The Master remembered the shot in the Agnew woods and that none had seen the hound since the moment he led the pack into that sombre forest. Not that night, nor the next, nor the next, did the champion come to kennels. The hills and valleys, the woods where the shot was heard, all the out-of-the-way places of a hunting country, were searched.

Three long years rolled by, and three years is much of a fox hound's life.

On Saturday, December 14th, 1929, I was lunching at the kennels with the Master. Rankin, the Huntsman, looked in and said, "Have you told him yet?" "No," replied the Master, "I have not told him. Will you bring him in Charlie?" A minute later Rankin led a hound into the room, a hound so distorted with fat that none but knowledgeable hound people would have known him even to be a hound. He had no neck. The magnificent head seemed to project out of fat shoulders. He waddled across the floor at Rankin's heels. About his neck he wore a collar giving his address as New Rochelle, New York. His stern swung back and forth in a smug, satisfied air as his once so sensitive nose now recognized the familiar conglomerate smell of domestic cooking. Sorrow was painted across Rankin's face. The Master walked towards the hound and spoke to him. The room was so silent I could hear a horse stamping in his stall at the far end of the hunt stable. The Master stood looking down at the hound, and while we watched Riley lifted his paw and offered to shake hands. We heard a throaty sound and our eyes turned to Charlie Rankin, fox hunter of Kentucky. "They have made a trick dog out of my hound," he said, and there was that in Charlie's eyes which boded no good to him who had done this to the best dog hound of 1926.

Charlie turned on his heel and left the room with Riley waddling after him.

On a crisp, fair winter morning we were drawing the River Hills. As we stood looking up the valley to the north a hound opened with a sharp, eager, decisive note. Riley had been drafted back into the pack.

CHAPTER XIII.

Mr. Flemming Moves Upstairs

I STROLLED over to Colonel Weatherford's to speak with him about a length of Page wire which Ed Simpson had stretched across Sloane Lane, closing the lane and throwing his north and south pastures into one. It was vital, when hounds were running, that we have the freedom of this lane which was the only passage through a series of deep swamps.

Ed Simpson was a bit temperamental, and the question of cutting a new wire fence and inserting a bar-way was one that must needs be approached tactfully.

When I arrived at the Colonel's, Eugène, the chauffeur, was waiting with the ancient Lancia car in front of the door, the engine humming softly. He asked me to confirm the correctness of his watch, shook his head, and prophesied one of those runs to the station at Poughkeepsie during which he was instructed not to hurry, — then told to get there in the quickest possible time. When in a hurry the Colonel would invariably warn Eugène against speed and reckless driving, pointing out the evils of such, then having performed what he thought to be his duty to the public, he would consult his watch, settle back in the car and tell Eugène to step along as smartly as he could. When the pace did not suit him he would invariably say, "God bless me, Eugène, don't doddle, don't doddle, the car isn't out of breath. Let us get on to wherever we're going."

Eugène, a typical son of France, revelled in all these scurries. They gave life its zest and twang. For years he had resisted a strong impulse to marshal his abundant savings and retire to his native Auvergne, but could not relinquish the exhilarating pastime of driving the Colonel.

He was a squat, square man of tremendous physique, with a thick mustache which he kept dyed a glistening black and waxed to a nicety. Possessed of a constant superabundance of energy he was forever polishing, brushing, sweeping, oiling, taking things apart and re-assembling them.

During a score of years he had acquired an assortment of uniforms worthy of a major-domo to Catherine of Russia. If time hung heavy he would indulge in a general whisking and pressing bee. It pleased him beyond measure to rush to his rooms between trips to the village and appear ten minutes later in black shoes and puttees, more glistening than those discarded, and with razor-like creases on coat and trousers.

He looked down upon all our native-born members of his profession, considering them totally unfitted for their calling. A local automobile accident always brought forth a deprecatory shrug, a shrug expressive beyond any spoken or written word.

His masterful approach to our local railway station was intended to be a condemnation of all American institutions and in particular to wither the spirits of American car-owners, their chauffeurs, all taxi drivers, station employees and members of the general public then in view. As is true of virtuosos it took very little to spoil Eugène's day. Should it prove that either the front or rear wheels of the car were above a certain number of inches from the station curb when the car came to rest or the door of the car was not on the axis of the station door, — that day counted for naught.

His one continual grievance lay in the fact that the Colonel would never let him drive a car to a Meet, and this the Colonel would not do because he had long since reconciled himself to the fact that employer and employee could never see eye to eye in this particular matter. Eugène's dominating thought was that he was a chauffeur to the master of the chase and at a Meet he invariably would engage in a competition international with all chauffeurs within striking distance. He was a discordant note in any pastoral setting. His assaults upon quiet farm yards furnished conversation in rural districts for a week after. Will Hatcher once showed me the wheel tracks of Eugène's car rounding his corn-crib and proved to me that there could not have been beyond an inch of leeway between the corner of the crib and Eugène's fender. Will Hatcher was not offended. He was simply interested. It was what he rather liked to envisage as a usual and conventional performance for Colonel Weatherford's French car driven by "that foreigner." "Only an inch, good God, Mr. Pendleton," said Will. But the fact remained that Eugène had driven the Colonel close to three-quarters of a million miles at home and abroad without so much as scratching a fender.

Leaving Eugène and his droning engine I entered the house and found those easily discernable signs of someone about to make a precipitous departure, — bags in the front hall; the Colonel's valet, Albert, running up and down stairs; Mrs. Penny, the housekeeper, fluttering from room to room; the butler thrusting a freshly-filled silver flask into

[197]

Albert's hand for insertion in the kit bag, an old and some-what shabby bag which the Colonel would not have exchanged for the finest modern example of the luggage-maker's craft.

The Colonel's two hundred pounds came clattering down the stairs. He shook hands, instructed Albert to give me a note which he had just penned to me, and said he would be back in a few days. Albert held his coat for him, the butler opened the door, Mrs. Penny said, "Pleasant journey, safe home, Sir," the Galway Blazer, stirred by the bustle, gave a couple of sharp barks, Eugène awoke the engine and away they spun out of the driveway.

I went to the library with Albert to find the note, which turned out to be a request that I take the Field pending the Colonel's return and not to let Will Madden, the Huntsman, draw Tom Beckworth's covert, for reasons which he would explain anon.

It dawned upon me that in the turmoil of his getting away I had not mentioned the Simpson matter to the Colonel, nor even inquired where he was going in such a rush, so I asked Albert, never imagining that there could be anything secretive about the trip.

Albert hesitated, a shadow of doubt crossing his face. "He didn't tell you, Sir?" "No," I replied. "Well, Sir," continued Albert, "you know how the Colonel is sometimes. It's about his old friend, Major Denning, that used to live up here. He died. You remember him, Sir. The Colonel didn't hear about it for some time and it's upset him a good deal. The Colonel set a lot of store by him, Sir. About an hour ago he sent for me and said that he couldn't find out anything about the Major's last days or where he had died, and that there seemed to be some mystery about it all, and that he couldn't have an old friend pass on that way. He told me to pack a bag for a week's trip and that he was leaving in three-quarters of an hour. I don't know where he is going, Sir, or why. It wouldn't seem any use going off on a long trip, maybe to Kentucky, after the Major had died. Please, Sir, don't mention that I talked with you about it. Colonel Weatherford will speak with you himself when he returns."

Strolling home across the pleasant fields separating my farm from the Colonel's my mind drifted back to the stately old gentleman from Kentucky who had once sojourned with us a few years in Millbeck.

I recalled his modest rooms at Mrs. Martin's house in the village, the imaginary trust estate, the Dulaney Denning trust estate, a vehicle of charity through which Colonel Weatherford and Jim Parkins dispersed a monthly stipend for living expenses, and a further very specific and plainly ear-marked stipend to satisfy the Major's uncontrollable urge to favor one horse above another.

I saw the old gentleman, tall, erect, white of hair, strolling our village street, followed by his diminutive, bare-footed colored boy, who always carried a basket for the Major's simple purchases.

He must have made a deep impression upon me to have caused so many little incidents connected with him to linger on in my memory — his pair of George III silver goblets in which he would so graciously mix and serve a julep, the eighteenth century tray on which the small colored boy would pass crackers and thin slices of cheese. These goblets and the tray were his only remaining possessions of value.

But above all I remembered the remark of our principal

[199]

village storekeeper, Mr. Maloney, who said to me after the Major had returned to Kentucky, "Mr. Pendleton, the old Major improved the hearts and manners of our whole village and some of those that live outside of it." I knew what Mr. Maloney meant and agreed with him, for there was a fine courtliness, a genuine concern for others, a gallantry and gentle simplicity about Dulaney Denning. If these things had been but surface mannerisms our keen, sharp Northern people would have soon detected the fact, but they were of the heart.

The misfortunes of our humblest citizens, irrespective of race or creed, aroused his sympathy. Hearing in the village of an accident, illness or death, the old gentleman would immediately call and offer his condolences. Many a cottage household was encouraged by his visits of good cheer.

My mind reverted to such events as the Major's concern when Mrs. Stavinski, the Polish woman who did his laundry, was severely injured by an automobile. The Major was never in funds nor did he enjoy over much local credit, so he called upon Squire Oakley's gracious lady, told her of the distressing accident to Mrs. Stavinski, "my estimable laundress," and requested access to the cutting garden. He was given the freedom of the garden then and at all times; thereupon the old Major gathered a small bunch of flowers to which he attached a note:

"Major Dulaney Denning expresses the hope that Mrs. Stavinski is progressing favorably and that she will accept these flowers with his compliments."

He delivered the flowers in person, continued every second day for a period of three weeks to gather fresh flowers for "my estimable laundress, Mrs. Stavinski," and each day wrote a word of cheer on his card.

Then memory jumped to the Major, mounted on Colonel Weatherford's ancient Welsh cob, judging the shooting dog trials down at the Verbankton Club, his fine, trained eye following the faults and achievements of the country's premier pointers and setters. Sportsmen liked his judging, for as Charles Landeer said to me, he seemed to sense and feel the problems which dogs pondered upon and thought for them and with them and made their perplexities his own.

Losers whose dogs had done well always went home with the remembrance of some thoughtful, courtly word of appreciation. "May I remark, Suh, that your dog's gallant performance today quite warmed my heart. My compliments, Suh." And to another, "Ah, Suh, what a brave dog to shoot over! The rascal makes me regret my years. Would you join me, Suh, in a drop of apple brandy to him? My compliments, Suh."

Reaching home that afternoon I ordered tea, and sat somewhat in reverie while I looked out of my west windows at the sun dropping slowly down to meet the cold, black crests of the Catskills.

The Major was judging the children's riding class at our horse show — little tots, all under eleven, some only four. I could see him doffing his black felt hat as he approached each small girl, "Would you back your mount for me, Miss Mary?" and the diminutive Mary striving to back her twenty-year-old woolly Shetland with a mouth hardened by generations of children. Mary's face grew red with doubt, vexation and embarrassment, and perchance her eyes commenced to fill, but the pony didn't back. "Splendid my dear, splendid. I didn't really want him to back but only to see how you would go about making him back. Thank you my dear.

He is a lovely pony and you ride him beautifully. Present my compliments to your mother and tell her she should be very proud of you." And so he would go down the long line of children, pleasing them and making them comfortable and happy.

And now he was no more. Many would wag their heads and call his a misspent life. Perhaps to have gambled away one's patrimony did constitute an error of judgment, but, I asked myself, how many of us journey on leaving so colorful and happy a record to make music in our memories.

I knew him only as he was slipping gently down into the dignity of years, but we spent many hours together under grey, somber autumn skies, watching and talking of the ritual of the seasons. Snatches of old conversations and sayings came back to me. He was telling of a hunting accident which kept him abed an entire season, yet would not for a moment have me condemn his mount. "It was only my horse's pre-occupation, Suh, in getting to the earth which caused the trifling misfortune. He was an airy horse, Suh, with the mark of bravery upon him."

The old Major was observant of nature's subtlest touches and would pause to comment upon them with interest and appreciation of their wonders and beauty — the greyness of ancient tree trunks; snow drifting down a November wind; a water-spider making her miraculous way across a tiny stream; willow branches stroking the river; the odors that early frosts bring forth from herbs; the color tones in animals when they stand between you and the setting sun. He caught these little things — the little things that make something more of a day afield than merely tramping and shooting. Such things are not empty chronicles of time.

He was somewhat of a stickler in respect to his sport, lamented the lack of the amenities and could not abide the inaccurate phraseology of modern youth. I once overheard him talking with Enid Ashley's youngest son who was shooting with us. "My dear young friend, three birds are not a lot of birds. Three birds constitute a leash of birds. Two birds are a brace, three birds a leash. A pair are those united by nature, a couple are those united by a couplet. You don't raise a woodcock, you flush it. You raise a grouse, and spring a snipe, and remember, it's not an army or a flock of plover. It's a wing of plover."

But of all tales and incidents which depicted the old gentleman's intuitive gallantry, I liked best the account, as told by Colonel Weatherford, of taking the Major salmon-fishing in Canada. Through some cause not clear to me the Major was furnished with a rod somewhat too light for the particular water assigned to him. In the course of the morning he hooked on to a fish acknowledged to be larger than a good man could well control in that pool, where a fisherman had little freedom.

The Major struggled valiantly and anxiously, putting all his skill and art into the contest. Suddenly the fish started to run. There was no holding him. Colonel Weatherford appeared on the scene, but thinking it better not to disturb the Major, remained in seclusion and watched the battle. Only a few yards of line remained on the reel. The end seemed inevitable. Then, in the very nick of time the fish turned and came up stream. As the huge salmon passed him the old Major removed his hat.

I heard my man coming quietly into the room and knew he would presently draw the curtains and turn on the lights.

The mountains had receded into the distant secrecy of the night. Out on the terrace the November wind was playing a solemn, plaintive psalmody against the angles of the house, driving the scurrying, restless leaves back and forth. Then it come to me in my musing that the wind was not just a casual, purposeless thing, for was it not helping each new fallen leaf to its final resting place? In the quiet hours of the night that wind would cease blowing and every leaf would lie close-nestled. They would have gone, not to death, but to re-incarnation, appearing ages hence as part of great trees enduring down through the aisles of time. And if this were true then certainly my old friend, in whatever far distant lonely spot he might have laid him down was also only waiting and resting. A delicate concept, of Mr. Berry, the wine merchant, of St. James Street, London, crossed my mind — an old, dead vine-leaf tucked away in the warm earth — waiting — and finally saying adieu to the last bottle of the vintage of its year. Who knows but when my time comes the old Major may not be waiting to say, "My compliments, Suh."

The Colonel returned at the end of a week. We hunted, dined, shot, and played bridge together, but never a reference was made to our old friend.

It came on to a hunting day in December. We had had a week of moderate frost and the going was not good. On the way to the Meet a fine drizzle set in. As the moisture reached the ground it froze, making the footing treacherous. There were only a handful of people at the Meet and I was rather hopeful the Colonel would return to kennels, — a wish somewhat fostered by my being on a green and rather uncertain fencer. Unless you have coursed our steep hillsides in winter you would not grasp the difficulties under which horses labor.

We drew the West Willow Bottom and Thockmorton coverts, and then, in crossing the uplands east of High Holden we apparently jumped a fox which was crossing over to Tim Anvil Woods. He went away for Bangdollen, crossed Marcy's stream over the fallen pine tree, raced on for Three Spires, turned east, and hounds dusted him along to the foot of Makepiece Ledges. He skirted the ledges, turned north, and hounds brought him for three miles to Westmoreland Bottom, at a trimming pace.

A quarter of a mile south of the Bottom the ground dips sharply down to the East Branch of Benhams Brook. Just before you get to the brook there is a set of bars standing on the steepest part of the hill. It is the sort of jump you must navigate slowly and with caution at any time and on any horse. Will Madden, the Huntsman, was laid up, and the Colonel was hunting hounds. He was riding his old reliable Athelstane, but because of the footing the Colonel was having difficulty in keeping on terms with hounds. This made him irritable and impetuous. I called out to him that if he would hold hard a moment I would lower a bar. He paid no attention to me, but pulled Athelstane down to a cautious trot and let him drop his head so that the old horse could work out his own problem.

A glance at the horse's demeanor and expression told of his mistrust. He trotted collectively down a steep and exceedingly slippery hill to a set of five fairly stout rails set close together and standing perhaps four feet, or an inch higher. His front feet left the ground preliminary to navigating the fence, — when suddenly his hind feet started to slide towards the fence. He gave the impression of trying to stop but was unable to do so, and so lurched forward with all four legs sprawled at different angles. The horse hit the second or third rail from the top and he brought the Colonel down, the Colonel never leaving his mount until they struck the ground. They were moving so slowly the Colonel could not get free.

Athelstane was on top and trying hard to get on his legs. In his efforts it looked as though his feet must have struck the Colonel a dozen blows. I jumped from my horse, threw the reins to Henry Newcombe, vaulted the fence and ran to my old friend. The horse was now free of him, but the Colonel lay on his face, his body twisted into a terrifying position. Mary Sedgwick and Pettybone Lithgow joined me. The first attempt to turn over so huge a man as John Weatherford, when you don't know what may be in store, has its gruesome aspects. His face was caked with mud and bore the marks of one of Athelstane's shoes. So much of his face as was discernible was grey.

I started to undo his stock, when to my astonishment I heard, "What in the devil are you doing, Pendleton? God bless me, have they caught the old horse? Who has gone on with hounds? Here, man, give me a hand."

There was no reasoning with him. We led Athelstane down into a gully, lowered the left stirrup, helped the Colonel as much as he would permit, and so got him mounted. He was bruised, severely shaken and evidently in considerable pain.

Hounds had made a left-handed loop and were running strongly towards a clump of woods some half a mile to our left. I shortened the Colonel's leather and rode slowly on with him. The cry of hounds was magnificent that day. The small patch of woods were ringing from end to end. Hounds were close to their fox. Suddenly a hoarse, quavering whisper emerged from somewhere under the Colonel's now turned up collar, "Damn it, Pendleton, cheer them man, cheer them. I can't make a whisper. The fox will never leave those woods. Cheer them. They will kill unless he finds an earth. Who is with them?" "George Ashley," I told him. "Come on, Pendleton. Come on. I think I can jog." But he couldn't, and there was no need of it, for we heard George Ashley's fine voice come rolling out of covert. The Colonel again tried to set his horse at the jog. "They've killed, Pendleton," he said, "they've killed, old man. God bless me, but they are an honest pack of hounds. Some people didn't want to hunt today. I wouldn't have missed it for a hundred-acre farm."

Nothing that I could say would dissuade the Colonel from entering the covert and poking on through to the kill, in spite of the fact that he was obliged to hold on to the breast-plate with his right hand to steady himself.

He and I then rode out to the Smithborough Pike, turned in at Jim Breed's, requisitioned a car, chauffeur and fur coat, telephoned Dr. McTavish to be at the Colonel's house, and then headed back to Millbeck. A less determined man would have winced at the movements of the car, for the old Colonel was battered and bruised from head to foot.

During all that long journey he made but one reference to his fall. "Pendleton," he said, "are you in a hurry to get home?" "No," I answered. "Well," he went on, "if it wouldn't inconvenience you would you stay around until I get off my left boot? I'll have trouble with that old jackass, Albert. They once had me on a stretcher in England, and God

[207]

bless me if Albert didn't cut one of the best boots in Europe. He has no spunk, Pendleton, no spunk. Wait until you see the way he carries on."

There was nothing broken or even unduly sprained other than the Colonel's left ankle, but such a continuous pattern of bruises has seldom greeted the medical eye. Athelstane was too full-made and formidable a horse to fall and lie on one, and then use one as leverage.

After his examination Doctor McTavish issued emphatic instructions. The Colonel was to stay in bed, keep quiet, if necessary take a sleeping potion and get to sleep as quickly as possible. The doctor then took Albert out in the hall for private instruction.

The Colonel asked me to close the door, then beckoned me to come over to him. "Go home and change, Pendleton," he whispered, "then come back. We'll dine up here. Hand me the cellar book — that's it in the red leather binder. Now, then, pick out what you think would do us the most good. Don't overlook the Chambertins. God bless me, but didn't the old horse give me a proper purler."

I was of two minds as to what to do, but finally concluded that a short visit with the Colonel would probably be better for him than leaving him to his own resources. There was no telling what form of recreation he might engage in, so I returned at about seven-thirty for dinner.

The Colonel was stretched out on a couch, resplendent in a blue satin bath robe. His left eye was practically closed, a large knob protruded from his forehead and his lips resembled those of the loser in a heavyweight championship fight.

Albert had set a small table for me in front of the fire and arranged an invalid's table over the couch for the Colonel.

During the long years of our friendship we had dined together countless times but never with greater content than on that evening. And yet I don't know what occasioned that content for the Colonel was not communicative, nor did I feel any urge to converse. We simply sat there in his snug dressing room, the lights lowered, sipping good wine and enjoying the flickering fire. I had a feeling that his thoughts were often far from Millbeck and that something sobering was revolving in his mind.

Albert removed the tables, brought the Colonel his pipe and a box of cigars, and placed a rugged, gnarled apple log on the fire. The Colonel tried a cigar but found smoking it uncomfortable, and requisitioned a light pipe with a thin stem. He lit the pipe, Albert left the room, and we sat smoking for some time, when the Colonel suddenly said, "Pendleton, Dulaney Denning died. I didn't tell you about it when it happened because I didn't know any of the details and was ashamed to confess the fact. I went down to look into the situation the other day and since my return I have felt upset and for some reason didn't want to talk about the matter.

"You see, Pendleton, he lost all of the money he won up here at Millbeck when his horse captured the Great American Stakes at Belmont. He lost it within two years after returning to Kentucky. He wouldn't appeal to me. He wouldn't or couldn't appeal to anyone in Kentucky, so he simply disappeared. No one knew where he went. I even employed a detective agency, but they couldn't trace him. I only heard of his death through a half-sister who wrote asking my financial help to have his body reburied in the family plot. I never could learn, even from her, what happened to him, so went down to find out for myself. I discovered where he had been living and where he died.

"There was a young lady in the place, a school-teacher, who had befriended him. I discovered her by accident. I liked her, Pendleton. I liked her very much. When I was leaving she looked up at me and said, 'Mr. Weatherford, you were very fond of Mr. Flemming?' 'Yes,' I told her, 'for nearly fifty years.' She hesitated, and then went on, 'Mr. Weatherford, I knew quite a good deal about his life here. Would you care to have me try and write a little account of it for you?'"

The Colonel sat musing as though of two minds, then reached under the pillow against which he was propped and extracted some typewritten sheets. "I had thought to read this over to myself first, Pendleton. It only came today, but if it would not be an imposition would you be willing to read it aloud? I would appreciate it. I want to hear it. I wonder if it was that fall and getting shaken up and feeling old that makes me keep thinking of the Major tonight."

It was a murky, unsightly, ill-favored town. The few, who had prospered at the expense of the many lived in large, hideous, stuffy houses on West Hill. Those who labored, when there was labor, lived under the Hill in unpainted houses on muddy, dead-end streets, working a week, laid off a week, in debt and with small hope.

Into this ill-conceived industrial center there drove one day in a shambling top-buggy a tall, elderly, distinguished-looking man somewhat frayed as to apparel. He had evidently traveled many miles. He arranged with the local livery stable-keeper to care for his old horse and buggy, and at the end of three or four days was ensconced in a small, unpainted, one-story cottage known locally as a shack, situated a few doors from the livery stable.

In time a small sign appeared in front of the house:

Mr. Flemming will be pleased to render service to those whose horses, dogs or other animals may be sick or injured.

There were very few horses maintained in the shadow of the mines and mills and in that town people did not concern themselves with the ills of their dogs. And so the "doctor," as he was beginning to be called, took to wandering off over the neighboring mountains, spending long days in his shambling old buggy, calling upon mountaineers and their families.

Time went on and news of his skill spread from one rock-strewn mountain farm to the next, and tall, spare, taciturn men would now and again ride into town seeking the old doctor, and he would hitch up and climb the rough, steep roads into the mountains.

No one on West Hill ever knew him or had even so much as heard of him, but those under the hill began to love and depend upon him. "Wasn't he a doctor?" they asked. "Didn't people say he was a doctor? Hadn't he helped so and so? And then he didn't send any bills, or call and ask for pay, or write letters. He just came and sat with you and said what he thought might do you good."

And so time rolled on but with it the doctor's affairs became ever more desperate. He traveled the roads day and night in larger and larger circles giving help where help was needed; but no one paid him. There was nothing to pay with. Mills and mines were closed. People couldn't pay. The mountaineers did what they could — a few eggs; now and then a pound of butter; occasionally a ham.

His landlord, the rent being long in arrears, asked him to vacate. The livery stable keeper learning of the situation offered him a small room over the stable, to which the doctor's few possessions were moved.

Fearing that those who might be in need of him might not be able to find him the doctor made a simple sign which with the consent of the livery-man he attached to the hitching post in front of the stable:

Mr. Flemming Has Moved Upstairs

And so this lonely, courteous old Samaritan traveled the mountains and muddy streets of the town through the long, hot days of summer and bitter days of winter, trying to help, trying to cheer, perhaps trying to forget, and striving in his proud old age to earn his living, any kind of a living, and preserve his independence.

People, as is the way of those who are hard pressed, learned to lean and call upon him more and more. The old mare was forever pulling the creaky wagon up into the mountain, and upon her return there was certain to be someone waiting hopefully in one of the dour, unpainted houses of the town.

Then there came a day when no one saw him. The old mare had not been taken out of the stable. The livery keeper went to look. Mr. Flemming had passed on.

Funds were required. The old mare and buggy were sold. A few simple veterinarian instruments were passed on for a song. A dozen or so books found buyers at ten cents apiece. The livery stable keeper contributed a dollar for an old goblet, a very old goblet, in which to stand his pen and pencils on his dusty, untidy and little used desk. Some thirty dollars were realized, a plot purchased at the cemetery, and the funeral arranged. No one knew where Mr. Flemming came from nor to whom he belonged.

While it was yet dark, mountain families were astir. Lights flickered from every cabin. Teams were hitched, saddles cinched, and in the still, quiet hours the mountaineers started their silent trek towards the town. It was a bleak, rain-swept day, yet they journeyed stoically on, the women riding in the wagons, the men on horseback or afoot.

Those from West Hill, sitting in their offices on High Street, looked out of their windows perplexed at the long stream of unfamiliar vehicles.

It was a drab and somber procession which later took its way through the deep red mud to the unkempt cemetery on the edge of the town. Mill-hands, mountaineers with their families, miners long out of work, walking side by side in the rain. At the head of the procession was the town drunkard, sober for the first time in a dozen years.

At the conclusion of the service someone said that the doctor should have a stone, that they couldn't leave him just that way. They took up a collection. People out of work have no money. Those who lived in the mountains lived by barter. Six dollars was all that even their affection could produce. Everyone who had anything gave, but what could be done with six dollars?

Suddenly the town drunkard stepped forward. He was a great, red-headed man whose strength had become a legend. "Wait," he said, and with that he started running back towards the town. People on the sidewalks stepped aside to let him pass and shook their heads and said he should be in gaol, but he ran on. Arrived at the livery stable, he put his powerful shoulders against the hitching post, shook it back and forth, pulled it this way and that, loosed it, jerked it out of the ground, put it on his great shoulders and ran back with it to the cemetery through the rain and mud.

The people gave way before him. He walked to the head of the grave, took a spade and set up the old hitching post.

Mr. Flemming Has Moved Upstairs

There seemed nothing for either the Colonel or me to say so we re-lit our pipes and sat smoking, but after a few moments the Colonel said, "Pendleton, I won't send the money to have him moved."

CHAPTER XIV.

Marian Ashley's Bespoken

I was taking tea with Enid Ashley when her four-year-old daughter, Marian, entered the room. "I hope," said Eunice, "that you have not been over to Colonel Weatherford's again." "Yes I have, Mummy," replied the young lady, "and I had some Cambridge tea and three cookies, and the Ternal showed me two baby woosters that fights that Eddie Walsh has, and told me a story and I told him two stories." Then Marian left the room intent on some concern of her own.

Enid watched her departure, smiled and looked over at me, saying, "What in the world can I do with that child? Not a day passes that she does not take herself over to the Colonel's and call upon him. It's the better part of a mile there and back across the fields, yet she trudges it nearly every afternoon. I have asked the Colonel's Albert to tell her that she is not to bother the Colonel and to send her home, but that does no good. And I have warned the Colonel to defend himself, but he seems quite incapable of coping with the situation yet sputters and becomes abusive if I threaten to forbid her calling on him.

"If the Colonel is not at home she walks right into the library, pulls down one of her favorite books and looks at pictures until he returns. If he is engaged she curls up on a

[215]

chair as close to him as she can get and amuses herself until he is free. Really, Pen, they are the most ridiculous couple you have ever seen together. There never were such conversations as they carry on."

As a matter of fact I knew a great deal more about this love affair of the Colonel's than did Enid herself, for I had dropped in on these tea parties more than once and had been put at my ease for all time through hearing Marian whisper to the Colonel, "We don't have to stop talking 'cause Mr. Pendleton came, 'cause Mr. Pendleton isn't company, is he, Ternal?"

Enid Ashley had four children. Three of them were keen, exuberant, every-day sort of children, spending their time dashing from one activity to another, riding, hunting, swimming, picnicing, and playing all manner of games. Little Marian, the youngest, was of a different ilk, exceedingly different. She was of the very woof and weave of the out-of-doors, of the good earth and of the things it brought forth. Her world centered in the fields, swamps and wooded hills surrounding her home, and in the things that lived in those fields. She was enamoured and continuously enthralled by her stage and the countless miracles enacted thereon.

Her power of observation was a source of wonderment to the Colonel. I recall her narrating the discovery of a brood of baby wood ducks, of her sitting motionless in the seclusion of an alder bush watching, recording and translating every act and movement of the duck and her young into terms of human motive and endeavor. From behind the alder bush she had witnessed the family's great adventure — the ever perilous journey from nest to water, and I recall the Colonel's interested expression as she, so tellingly, described the flutter and anxiety of the mother, the impetuous helter, skelter progress of the young, and of their wild first flight across the pond — skimming its surface, and "looking, Ternal, like puffy things blowed by the wind." The Colonel turned to me, saying, "God bless me, Pendleton, there is no authoritative book on duck one-half so illuminating."

The farm and its environs, teeming with exciting events, the birth of a colt, the arrival of new kittens, a new-born lamb, birds being hatched in every hedge and tree, — these caused the days to be too short, the nights too long.

One must find a confidant for such gripping, vital experiences. They must be recounted and enlarged upon. She discovered by accident that the Colonel was an ideal outlet. He himself was a competent naturalist and painstaking observer. He never laughed at, but only with, her. He asked crisp, meaningful questions. He argued and differed. He permitted a certain amount of whimsicality and enjoyed it, but not nature faking. He knew nothing of children and had no means of measuring their limitations, and would now and again burst out, "Nonsense, Marian, nonsense, fiddlesticks, tommyrot. That's not the reason young pheasants do that," and then he would explain the matter at issue, and Marian would look up at him with those big, thoughtful grey eyes of hers and think about it; and later he would probably ring for Albert to bring him his hat and stick and walk home with her half-a-mile across the meadows.

With the advent of school her visits became ever less frequent, but as her horizon broadened she called upon him for new interpretations. She turned to books, and he led her by suggestion to the New England school which was his own background. I could never quite forgive him for showing self-consciousness when discovered reading to her. He would close the book with a bang of finality, announcing that it was high time she ran away home, and she would look at him, hurt and disappointed and perplexed.

He finally overcame this insofar as I was concerned, and I look back with a good deal of contentment to some of those readings aloud. While she was still a wee tot he read and re-read the fine, earthy things of Dallas Lore Sharp. I once sat with them in his library on a grey, somber November afternoon, she curled up on the sofa beside him. They had both heard a great flight of geese pass over the night before, and chided me for missing the event. The Colonel turned to Professor Sharp's book.

"Honk, Honk, Honk. Out of the silence of the November night, down through the depths of the darkened sky, rang the call of the passing geese . . . . The stars shone clear in the far blue; the trees stood dark on the rim of the north and south; close up against the distant sky the wild geese were winging.

"Honk, Honk, Honk. . . . ordered as the tramp of soldiers . . . the flock swept over and was gone. They had summoned us and we had heard the wild sky-call, had heard and followed them through the dark of the night, up into the blue vault under the light of the stars.

"Round and dim swung the earth below us; hushed and asleep in the soft arms of the night. Hill and valley lay close together, farm-land and wood-land, all wrapped in the coverlet of the dark. City and town, like watch fires along the edge of a sleeping camp, burned bright on the rivers and brighter still on the ragged line of the shore and sea, for we were far away near the stars. The mountains rose up, but they could not reach us; the white lakes beckoned, but they could not call us down, for the stars were bright, the sky coast was clear, the wind in our wings was the keen, wild wind of the north, and the call that we heard — Oh! Who knows the call? Yet, who does not know it — that distant, haunting call to fly, fly, fly? . . .

"Honk, honk, honk! Oh, may I be awake to hear you, ye strong-winged travelers on the sky when ye go over northward calling all the south to follow you through the broken ice gates of the north.

"Honk, honk, honk! The wild geese are passing — southward."*

The Colonel closed the book. Marian was looking up at the ceiling and through it and up into the blue vault under the light of the stars, and I knew then why he loved her.

When very young and before one has learned that one does not hold converse with Masters of Fox Hounds when hounds are hunting, she used to ride up to the Colonel and engage him in all sorts of discussions. I remember a Thanksgiving day. It had been an eminently unsatisfactory and exasperating morning. The whole world and its wives were out — everything inhabiting the town of Millbeck was out except the foxes, and if they were out certainly hounds could get no wind of them. Miss Marian Ashley had not been among those present at the Meet, probably having been engaged upon some important matters of her own at that hour. About noon, as we were standing on Highminster with hounds half-heartedly drawing Three Spires Upland cover, I saw the young lady approaching across the fields on her twenty-year-old Shetland pony, a fat, long-haired, somnolent little

* Quoted by permission of Houghton Mifflin Company.

mount that required the constant application of Marian's heels to keep it in motion. A group of perhaps a dozen of us were standing close to Colonel Weatherford, but sensing that his present mood would not be sympathetic towards coffee-housing, particularly as one hound was speaking in a desultory voice to a night line, — we were keeping discreetly silent.

Marian finally accomplished her tortuous journey, wove her pony through us, her short little legs kicking back and forth to give encouragement to Fluffy Miller, and rode up to the Colonel, without his being so much as conscious that she was in the field. "Ternal," she said, "it's most rooféd over but it's another one. It's bigger than the other one. They didn't like that one. 'Member, I told you it was orful wet 'cause when the ice isn't slippery and won't go over the dam the water goes back and back and covers that place 'cause Mr. Thingamabob and me went out in the boat Christmas to help the ice get over the dam, but the new one is dry." And the Colonel scowled and figuratively scratched his head and looked down at her and muttered, "God bless me," then recalled that this all had to do with the muskrats building their winter home on the edge of Enid Ashley's swamp, an operation which Marian was following with solicitude. There then followed a really knowledgeable dissertation on the architectural and dietetic habits of the lonely muskrat.

When the domestic problems of the muskrats had been disposed of I saw Marian touch the Colonel on the knee, then beckon to him with her finger in a most secretive yet emphatic manner.

It is no simple task to bend down from a seventeen-hand horse and hold private converse with a very diminutive young lady on an eleven-hand pony, but the Colonel gallantly went his part of the journey and Marian stood up in her stirrups. None of us heard what was said, but we did hear the Colonel say, "How do you know?" Then there was more whispering, at the conclusion of which the Colonel turned to John Donalds and asked him if he would go into the covert and tell Will Madden to bring hounds to him as quickly as he could.

There was a tinge of ill will towards fox hunting that Thanksgiving Day on the part of the non-hunting members of certain families. But a turkey is still a turkey, though he be a bit over-done. Stable-boys crept home over the sixteen miles from North Bangdollen to Millbeck on tired horses, with the evening star as a beacon.

This friendship continued on through the years and the Colonel watched and meditated upon her growing up as an old philosopher might have sat on his Ionian terrace contemplating the youth of Greece.

In the spring of Marian's twelfth year a thoroughbred filly was foaled on Enid Ashley's place, a filly that should have been of great promise. She was out of a distinguished and royally-bred mare and by a Domino horse of great promise. Yet a poorer, less promising foal never disfigured the hills of Dutchess County. It was weak, stringy, crooked-legged, and of dreary aspect. When a few days old its nose began to swell and an examination disclosed a stoppage of the air passage. The obstruction was removed but the enlargement remained, giving the filly the appearance of having the lower half of an acute Roman nose, and contributing further to her forlorn appearance.

After the lapse of a few months Enid telephoned asking if the Colonel and I would come over and help her to decide whether or not she should put the filly away. Enid's major perplexity lay in the fact that Marian, by very reason of the filly's forlornness had adopted and mothered it since birth. A word of scorn, ridicule or even mild criticism directed toward the filly would cause a moistening of Marian's eyes. I once overheard her stamp her foot and ask one of her brothers whether if he was sickly and little and full of worms he would like people to laugh at him?

The Colonel was primarily practical and pointed out to Enid that in view of her straitened if not almost desperate financial condition she had no right to raise a foal of so little promise. In this I concurred, adding that the filly would never stand training.

The Colonel and I left Enid's farm and went down into Hawk's Hollows to try an hour or two of late afternoon fishing. We came off the stream about seven-thirty, located the Colonel's car and were about to enter it when we saw a note resting on the seat addressed to the Colonel. He opened it, read it and sat sitting with it in his hand, entirely forgetful that we had a good dinner awaiting us at home. He finally put the letter in his pocket, started the car, and drove slowly along. When we had gone perhaps a hundred yards he blurted out, "God bless my soul, Pendleton, did you ever commit murder? Did you ever contemplate it? Were you ever accused of it?" "No," I said, "not openly." "Well read this," he growled, handing me the letter, and I read.

I will say of the Lord, He is my refuge and my fortress. In him will I trust. Surely he shall deliver (my filly) from the snare of the fowler and from the noisome pestilence.

Please think of these words.   Marian Ashley."

I returned the note without comment.

Summer slipped softly into early fall. The days shortened and before I knew it another year had rolled around to crisp November.

I was standing in my lower pasture looking over a herd of Black Angus steers, when Eddie Walsh, the Colonel's groom, appeared in the distance letting down a bar-way preparatory to leading a horse through. At a loss to know why he should be pursuing this particular course to the Colonel's stable I stood watching him, and presently recognized Marian Ashley's filly, now known as "Bespoken." Eddie was having a trying and exasperating adventure. The filly was barely halter-broken and decidedly unwilling to accompany him.

When opposite to me Eddie gave his cap a vicious jerk, saying, "I'm sorry, Sir, to be trespassing, but it's herself like to destroyed me when Maloney's truck come along. She's just after bein' weaned, and I'm takin' her over to the boss's stable. It's nothing he'll have out of her, not by no manner of means, 'cause there's nothing to her at all at all." Eddie having regained his breath the tussle proceeded.

As this uncongenial couple finally passed from view I could but smile at the mess the Colonel had undoubtedly let himself in for. He had never, during all the years I had known him, raised a colt on his place, insisting that such a procedure was unfair to the colt and equally unfair to one's own pocketbook, and that if one wanted to breed and raise a colt one should give it the advantages of Virginia or Kentucky.

He had no suitable enclosure nor even a companion for a freshly-weaned foal, and nothing is drearier than a colt out in a pasture alone through the long hours of the day.

Within the week I was hacking home from hunting and

turned off at the Colonel's driveway to slip across his stubble field and so save myself a few steps when, in passing the orchard, I saw the dreary, brown wisp of a filly standing under an apple tree with her head nestled close up to James T. Twitcher, Hopie Hanger's diminutive spotted mule, which the Colonel must have borrowed to keep the filly company.

Had I seen those incongruous lovers in the Colonel's library I could not have felt greater surprise than finding them in the orchard. This small planting of apple trees was an adjunct to the Colonel's garden and an object of great pride to him. No orchard in Dutchess County was watched over with such constant zeal. Experts appeared annually to prune, paint, scrape, cement and fertilize. Other experts followed at various periods to spray. The ground was tilled, planted, plowed under and further fertilized until the stand of grass was so formidable that a setter could barely force his way through. And here was this orchard, forming as it did the southerly end of a beautifully landscaped garden, turned into a paddock for an unsightly filly foal and a spotted Kentucky mule. That the mule was one of the best conveyances across the Millbeck country hardly justified this excess.

While I mused upon this phenomenon old Pat Dwyer, the Colonel's stud groom, appeared with some feed. Upon recognizing me he looked chagrined, but thinking to make the best of the situation, said, "It's breeding we're going into, Sir. These be our first two. A fine big filly this, Sir. We don't let her out when it's windy. She blew over the fence Monday week." Then old Dwyer's face changed. "What would you think Colonel Weatherford would want with the like of this, and she standing here where all his friends got to see her as they go up to the house. It was Squire Oakleigh himself come

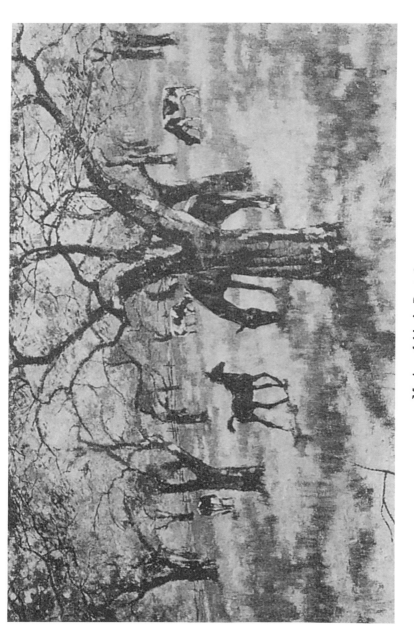

Marian Ashley's Bespoken

by yesterday to see the boss and stops, same as you, while I was feeding her, and says, 'What's that, Dwyer,' and courage wasn't in me to say yes or no to him.

"And Mr. Pendleton, you wouldn't know the half of how the boss be carrying on. He writes Major Beard down to Kentucky and wants to know where does he get the hay and oats he was telling the Colonel about at Saratoga — Michigan or Canada I think it was, and we got some of them. You wouldn't see the like of them at the Ascot meeting. Forty-six pound oats, and the color of the sun in them; and cod liver oil and I wouldn't know what. And everything wrote out on one of these writing machines. It's wrote out like this, 'A horse's stomach is small in proportion to the size of the animal. They should be fed moderately but frequently. You will feed a fourth time between nine and ten o'clock at night.' And would you look at the filly, Sir."

I rode home thinking somewhat upon a dreamy little girl and a practical, worldly-wise old sportsman, concluding that probably much of the world's destiny was governed by affection.

The following September Marian went away to school, a project that strained her mother's resources to the danger point. She was the youngest of the family, and Enid could not bring herself to deprive the child of the advantages which the older brother and sisters had enjoyed. It was also recognized that intellectually Marian was better qualified to profit through education than the other members of the family. I gathered in a roundabout way that the Colonel had asked the privilege of assisting but that this had been refused. Upon the completion of her first year it became evident that Marian's prospects of ever getting to college, upon which she had set her heart, were practically nil. The Colonel stormed and took Enid Ashley to task, telling her in round language that she had no right to let pride and pig-headedness stand in the child's way, but Enid could not bring herself to permit what would have been a seven-year obligation on the Colonel's part. The Colonel stuck out his lower jaw, tugged at his long white mustache, and couldn't for the life of him understand how he could be defeated in what looked to be so simple an issue.

On a raw, bleak March afternoon, just as the Colonel was getting ready to skip off to Europe, he called me up asking if I could drop in on him. When I arrived he was leaning on the orchard fence, wrapped up in a great-coat, and gazing at the Bespoken filly.

He instructed Walsh to slip a saddle on the filly and follow us to a long, flat meadow in which he had installed two white poles, three furlongs apart. Walsh was told to take the filly to the far pole and let her step on until he had passed the finish pole. The Colonel asked me to stand where I could get an advantageous view of the filly while extended. He himself stood opposite the finish line with a stop watch. Walsh went down to his position and at a signal from the Colonel opened the filly up. At the conclusion of the trial the Colonel walked up to me, saying, "Pendleton, did you see what I saw?" "Yes," I answered.

We adjourned to the Colonel's library, warmed our backs at his ample wood fire and stood for some time, neither of us speaking. The Colonel took out his watch, stood looking at it, pressed the spring, and the curtain was rung down on Bespoken's trial. He looked quizzically at me, then rang for a servant and ordered a bottle of his rarest Madeira.

He sat toying with his glass, then asked me if my old trainer, Jim Andrews, was at Belmont Park, and how he could be reached. I told him. He poured himself another glass of wine, stood with his back to the fire a moment, then manned the telephone and requisitioned Jim Andrews. At the conclusion of the conversation I said good-bye to the Colonel and wished him a safe journey, for he was leaving for town in the morning and sailing the day following.

Some two weeks later I received a letter from Jim Andrews which required an entire evening to answer. Good trainers have a great deal of pride, and Jim Andrews' pride had been hurt. I take credit for having persuaded him not to ship the filly back to Millbeck, but it took all of my persuasiveness. There was no equine fault known to horsemen that was not attributed to that filly. Andrews ended his letter by saying, "and the Colonel wants me to get this straight pasterned, asthmatic rabbit tight and slip her in some place to win $1500 for a little girl that he says needs the money terrible bad. Lord A'mighty, Mr. Pendleton, she don't look or act as though she could last three furlongs out in the brush with sixty pounds on her."

I worried through a long, cold, late spring, then, as the owner of a two-thousand-acre farm, entered the busiest time of the year for me and had no chance to dwell upon little Marian, her filly, or Jim Andrews.

The Colonel returned from abroad about the middle of June. As soon as he caught up with his affairs he turned his attention to Jim Andrews and asked me if I had heard anything from him, to which I replied "No." Then he said he couldn't understand why he had not heard anything and did not see why Jim had not started the filly. He had apparently written Andrews but received only an indefinite and unsatisfactory reply. At the end of another week he telephoned to him, but heard nothing definite or encouraging. Finally he suggested that we have a day's racing.

We went down to the track, located Andrews, and asked for information. Andrews is as conservative a man as I know, and far from being loquacious, except when excited. He sat chewing the end of a straw for some time, then said, "Colonel Weatherford, I don't know just what to say. I didn't want to talk over the telephone the other night for a lot of reasons, and didn't know rightly how to write you. The truth is, Colonel, I want to start the filly in the $30,000 Belmont Oaks." The Colonel jerked his head up and stared at Andrews. "God bless my soul, bless my —" "Yes, Colonel," Jim went on, "I know you'll think I'm crazy, and I guess I am. I don't want you to think that I put a whole lot of store by this filly. I don't. She's the hardest thing to train that ever came into my stable, but I'd like you to gamble the expense of letting me start her."

Jim paused to let this announcement sink in and then went on, "You see, Colonel, I'm not sure that she has more than one race in her. I don't mean breaking down, but she's terrible touchy. She don't like strange horses anywhere near her. If one of them bumps or crowds her she won't run — won't even run up any place near them. Lots of times she won't even pass a horse that she stables next to and knows well. Now, I'm telling you all the bad about her, — but Colonel, listen, she can run. Take my word for it, she can run. I wouldn't want to saddle anything for that race that wouldn't do you any good, or the little girl that owns her any good, or me any good, but Colonel, the filly can run. The only thing is I don't know whether I can get it out of her or not. Most of the time she has me licked.

"If I tell the boys in my string to let her get away on top, she steps along, but she is a slow starter, and if the other horses get away on top it's the devil's own job to get her home. I've tried everything I know and asked every old timer on the track, but she has them all stumped. She can run, if we can get it out of her. I have never started her because I didn't see the use of starting her in a cheap event. Maybe she'd get bumped and sour — then we are through. I thought we might as well head her for a real stake and take a chance that we could get her away on top and see if she would coast home."

Belmont Park on a day of great expectations. A day of sunshine, sparkle and fair breezes. A day when people have lunched well and thrown off their concern for the ills of the world at large and become indifferent to their own more personal trials. A day when flags and little pennants wave gaily with never a thought of a wind that some day is bound to change. An afternoon when the lawns are at their greenest, the balcony petunias at their gayest. When all the world is at play, afloat and ashore, from the yachtsman off Marblehead to the fox hunter in the Piedmont of Virginia.

It was on such a day that we walked out to the paddock at Belmont Park, Enid Ashley, Marian, Colonel Weatherford, Jim Andrews and I, a hopeful but not very expectant group.

Marian was silent and tense and drawn, much too tense and much too silent. She had eaten practically nothing at luncheon and had sat during the meal with her hands folded on her lap and looking straight ahead of her.

When we reached the paddock a boy was walking the filly around. She looked thin, wasp waisted, plain beyond description, and, I thought, dreary and unhappy. Someone came up to Jim Andrews and told him the odds were 30 to 1. The race was quite generally conceded to one of two fillies, Lady Jessamine and a chestnut by High Time.

Our filly was walking past us when Marian called softly, "Bespoken." The filly halted and stood as though fastened to the ground, turned her head, looked, then started toward us. The boy pulled her head towards him and she followed him, but almost immediately again turned her head towards us. When she again came around she stopped. Marian asked the boy to wait a moment and went up and spoke to the mare. Andrews was standing nearby, his hawk eyes taking in the whole performance. The boy started on with the filly but she insisted on stopping and turning her head around and trying to get back to the child.

Trainers loathe and mistrust anything out of the ordinary. People who were passing and repassing from the inspection of one or another of the horses began to notice the little pantomime and were congregating around us. The mare was becoming more determined and insistent. The saddling bell sounded and Jim Andrews stepped forward and started to saddle. He was plainly upset. The mare had been dull and indifferent during her entire training. Now she would not even stand to be saddled and was breaking into a sweat. Colonel Weatherford sensed the situation and told Marian to go over to her. Andrews, due entirely to being upset, resented this, but the instant the child reached the mare's head she ceased fretting.

Among the spectators was old Uncle Joe McPherson, the

well-loved and respected dean of American trainers. McPherson was fond of Jim Andrews, had been interested in the filly's peculiarities and had tried to help and counsel Andrews in her training. He had come over to see her saddled, having nothing of his own in the big stake.

As soon as Jim had the saddle on he hurried over to the old man and I heard him say, "Uncle Joe, I don't like the looks of things. I don't like them worth a damn. That filly is all upset."

Old McPherson removed a cigar from his mouth, flipped the ash off, and squinted up his eyes. "Jim," he said, "it's the little girl. That filly is lonesome and unhappy. Maybe when she was very young she sort of took to the child. She's never been contented since you had her at this track. She's not thrifty. Some horses do good at one track, some at another, or maybe she's never been right since she was foaled. You got any money on her?" "A hundred," said Jim. "Your people got any on her?" "No," replied Jim. "The Colonel has no faith in her, and Mr. Pendleton only has a hundred." "Well, Jim," went on the old man, "you hedge if you can."

The two men stood waiting for the saddling bell. Finally McPherson turned to Andrews, "Son, let me tell you something. Horses can't manage more than one idea at a time. Mark my word as to that. It don't take anything much to get their minds off the one thing you want 'em to do. Of course, your filly may get that little girl out of her mind as soon as she gets with other horses, but maybe she won't. I've saddled a few horses in my time and I've seen horses looking around at some woman for sugar, but I never saw a horse carry on like that filly is carrying on over that little girl, and no one else ever did. She's like as not to never leave the post, or hang back and run crooked and weave all over the track with her mind mostly on getting back to this paddock. Why, Jim, a circus trainer told me he wouldn't let the boy who fed his horses stand any place near where they were performing because the horses were apt to get their minds off the act and spoil the show if they saw the boy. It don't look good for the filly, Jim."

The mounting bell sounded. Jim went over and spoke with his boy aside and gave him a leg up, but his face was dour and gloomy. We climbed to the stand in rather a sepulchral attitude, taking Andrews with us. Walking up the stairs the Colonel took my arm, saying, "God bless my soul, Pendleton, what an unconscionable lot of grief we bring on ourselves. Why in the world did I want to bring that child down here today. God bless me, why did I ever want to put the filly in training in the first place?" Knowing no good reason I kept silent. The fillies paraded up and down in front of the stand, then to the starting post. I marvelled as I always did on the size and fullness of many of our modern day thoroughbreds, and thought what two hundred years of feeding and selecting had made of the progeny of the little Arab horse. The two short-odd fillies might well have been taken for mature animals. They were statuesque, powerful, rangy, racing machines, bred and owned by stables which had spared neither money nor effort to produce the very best.

There was an interminable delay at the post due to the High Time filly's impetuousity and unchristian attitude towards her neighbors. She finally lost her position and was moved to the outside. The Bespoken filly was restless, and I saw with some misgiving that she kept turning her head and occasionally her shoulders toward the saddling paddock. Andrews caught the situation through his glasses and his comment would ill fit this page. He finally put his glasses down and said to me under his breath, "The jig is up, Mr. Pendleton. There she is in fourth position, sandwiched in between two fast fillies. She ought to be on the outside. They'll get the jump on her. There will be a lot of crowding and jostling. Some of the fillies on the outside will bear over towards the rail. She'll be in a pocket. Somebody will bump her. She won't go through, and by the time the boy gets her over to the outside of the track and free of the other fillies, so she isn't scared, the Lady Jessamine filly will be home and unsaddled. The mare's all upset, Mr. Pendleton. She looks to me like for two cents she'd run through the rail maybe and break her neck just to get back to the paddock. Don't it seem queer to you, Mr. Pendleton, about that little girl and the filly. It seems queer to me."

While Jim was talking they were off and we trained our glasses. If Jim Andrews had been gifted with divine prophecy he couldn't have foretold the details of that start more accurately. This was a race for very young, very sensitive, very keen and very inexperienced race horses. There was jostling, crowding, squeezing, and our poor little undersized, self-conscious filly was sandwiched in the thickest pocket of the mêlée, being bumped, jostled and crowded. They all raced on together. Those from the outside pressed towards the rail, seeking the shortest route home. The Belmont Oaks and thirty thousand dollars were at stake.

I heard Colonel Weatherford mutter, "She can't slow up. She doesn't dare. They would step right over her. She's got to run until they have all passed her." Jim Andrews on the other side of me was asking the world at large, but in a semi-whisper, how in hell could she get out of that pocket even if she wanted to. "Damn it, Mr. Pendleton, she just can't get anywhere, she — why, why, why — look at her — she's starting to slow up already. Why, hell, look at her. She's quitting and they aren't to the three furlong pole."

The filly was plainly dropping back. Her quarters came into view, then her jockey, finally her head. She was alone and in the ruck. She hung for a few strides, then bore away from the rail —away from the other fillies, and kept that position for a dozen strides. Suddenly Jim Andrews touched my arm. "Mr. Pendleton, she's, she's, she's doing something. Look! She's started to come up — sure she is — she's picked up half a length. Lord A'mighty! Look! She's on terms with 'em again. What's she doin? What's she doin', Mr. Pendleton?"

There was a group of nine fillies bunched very close together — the ruck of the field. Ours was to one side of these — to the outside of the track, but on terms with them. In front of these nine were two fillies racing side by side and battling every foot of the journey, and three lengths ahead of these were Lady Jessamine, the High Time filly, and a black filly, all setting a sizzling, killing, heart-breaking pace — a pace that just crucifies a contender coming up from behind.

The money of the day was largely on the Jessamine filly, but High Time's daughter had many staunch supporters. They said that if the totals of that day's wagers had ever been published, the baseball magnates, who resent the crowds at Metropolitan tracks, and the reform element would have had ammunition enough to swamp Albany.

The race was proceeding to the satisfaction of thirty thousand people, for the leaders were increasing their advantage. An old-time member of the Jockey Club in the next box said to his neighbor, "They'll break the record for the Oaks."

Suddenly a man with a roar in his voice blurted out, "What's that coming up on the outside?" The Bespoken filly had stuck her nose beyond the six or seven who were still running together. In the next stride or two she was clear of them. The two just ahead of our little mare, who were fighting, straining, struggling to get on terms with the leaders, were three lengths ahead of her. The man with the voice hollered out, "She's walking — she's walking up on them. Look at her. It's that peewee filly of Jim Andrews'. Look at her! Look at her!"

Our little mare! She looked not more than a wisp of a shadow, squatting, digging in those ill-formed feet, straining her straight pasterns and fighting for her head — that dull, dreary, tragic head of hers. Jim Andrews in his tenseness grabbed my arm. "Good God, Mr. Pendleton. Do you see that? Do you see it? Do you see it? She wants to run. I never saw her grab for her head that way. She wants to come home. Hold her out, boy, out by herself. Oh, God keep her out — keep her alone. Look, look. Look at that, Mr. Pendleton. She's caught those two fillies. That's the Man-of-War filly on the rail — she can fly, and my filly has caught her. Now boy, go after them — go after the favorites. Lord A'mighty, don't run her into the ground. I never thought I would see her want to run that way. Those two top fillies are flying, Mr. Pendleton."

I could hear the Colonel breathing hard to the left of me. Marian was standing with both hands on the back of a chair in front of her. Jim's elbow touched me. "Look! Look! Mr.

Pendleton. She's picked up a length. She's walking. I tell you she's walking. They have only a sixteenth to go. Look at her. The black filly is through. She's beat. Let my filly step on, boy. Don't choke her. I never won a Belmont Oaks. She'll catch 'em, Mr. Pendleton — she, — she, — she, — she's caught 'em, she's caught 'em — she's fighting for it — and, Oh, God, she's only a pony. They can't stop her — she, she, she's burning 'em out —she's past 'em, past 'em. She — she, Oh, God, she's won, Mr. Pendleton!"

I don't know when Jim Andrews left us, but when I turned to speak with him he was gone. We waited for the fillies to canter back to unsaddle. Out of the corner of my eye I saw the Colonel comparing the official time with his own stop watch. He then returned his glasses to their case with a brisk click, extracted a cigar from his pocket, removed the band, put his expansive arm around Marian's shoulder, and patted her gently. "Well done, old girl, well done. We'll have a private suite at Smith College and a diamond-studded chafing dish."

The fillies were returning. Bespoken was cantering collectedly, alertly, with her head into her chest, but still looking only a wisp of a thing. A man back of me said to his neighbor, "She's a game little thing. She took the longest route home. She kept trying every foot of the journey. She belongs to old Colonel Weatherford, who used to race some good 'chasers. He never was a man to bet against. Jim Andrews says she really belongs to some little girl that's taking some kind of a beating. I lost fifty because of her, but hell!"

The jockey stopped her in front of the stand and raised his whip for the signal to dismount. The filly had not come to a halt before she wheeled around, looked towards the saddling paddock and whinnied. The Colonel was in the act of lighting his cigar and had the match in mid-air, when the filly whinnied. He shook the match out unused, held the unlighted cigar in his left hand and started stroking his chin with his right. As the filly was being led away he turned to me: "Pendleton, I detest nature-faking and all efforts of misguided people to attribute motives, reason and this and that to animals, but God bless my soul, I can't fathom that filly's actions and performances today any more than I can fathom some phases of the child who owns her. Look at Marian." I looked beyond the Colonel. The child was standing very straight, her head thrown slightly back, her hands crossed in front of her, gazing over the heads of the people beyond her, out into the endless blue of the sky. She was not at Belmont Park, nor is it for me to say where she was. As I watched her standing there, oblivious of all around her, a feeling crept over me that the result of that race was a thing she had asked for, and that her life, her thoughts, her motives, her faith, her attitudes had all qualified her to step resolutely forward, her head up, her grey eyes clear and confident, and say with the simplicity of childhood, — I want this thing.

As the filly passed through the gate we moved slowly down to visit with her. Enid Ashley and I walked together. I don't remember what we talked about, probably nothing very much, but I recall Enid saying, "Pen, do you remember that little note Marian wrote to the Colonel? It was odd, wasn't it? You know, Pen, she seems much closer to the big fundamental forces than most of us. The Colonel says it comes from being so much alone in those swamps and woods of hers. 'I will say of the Lord, He is my refuge and my fortress.' Life must be very simple and clean-cut to her, Pen."

When we reached Jim Andrews' stable the filly was being cooled out. Jim saw us approaching and came toward us. He removed his old brown hat. Jim Andrews is a fine looking individual, with a deeply bronzed face, strong crinkly hair tinged with grey, and exceedingly blue eyes surrounded by innumerable little wrinkles. He walked up to Marian with that brisk, vigorous, outdoor way of his and held out his hand, "I'm right glad your filly did so good, Miss Marian. She ran fine for you. Uncle Joe says it was the gamest race run this year at Belmont Park. I will do the best I can with her for you, and wish you a lot more luck."

Marian thanked Jim Andrews in a way that would have lingered long in my memory had I been Jim Andrews, and from an odd, serious look that stole across Jim's face I think it must have lingered long with him. She then touched my arm, hinting that she wanted to speak with me apart. "Mr. Pendleton," she said, "please tell me. Do you think Colonel Weatherford wants to race Bespoken any more? Do you think he would be hurt or disappointed if I asked to have her sent home to Millbeck. I don't want to ask him if you think it would disappoint him. You see, I don't want him to send her home just because I want her, but Mr. Pendleton, she's terribly unhappy at the track. She's not a racehorse. She never will be. I know her so well and know what she thinks of crowds and the other horses. She may not even be happy hunting. I don't think she will, but I can just poke about on her the way I do in vacations. She'll be happy with me and we'll watch spring coming at Easter and potter through my swamps at Christmas. I'm not putting it very well, Mr. Pendleton, but I want her home more than I have ever wanted anything in all my life. You don't know how she tried for me today. I don't dare go up to visit with her. I can't leave her here with all these strangers after today. Shall I ask the Colonel, Mr. Pendleton?" "No, Marian," I said, "Let me think it over a minute."

I didn't want to speak to the Colonel in front of Marian so secretly scribbled a note on the back of a card, giving him the picture, and slipped it to him while he was talking to Andrews. He glanced at it, and a thunderstorm, threatening to become a cloudburst, crossed his face. He showed the card to Andrews, and then took a turn of the turf in front of the stable. On his return Marian and her mother were talking to Jim. The Colonel joined the group, saying, "Marian, we should get the filly home. You mustn't let her eat up your profits. Jim, get a van tomorrow and ship her to Miss Marian Ashley, Millbeck, New York."

Marian walked up to him, started to say something, seemed uncertain how to get started, took hold of one of the buttons on his coat, turned it slowly, then looked up at him smiled and said, simply, "Thank you, Ternal."